International Baccalaureate
Physics
Higher Level

Introduction

This guide has been designed for students to use as a set of revision notes. All areas of the syllabus are covered and explained in a clear and simple way. Many examples are provided and worked solutions are given at the back of the text.

You should annotate and add notes to this guide where necessary – that is why the large margins are provided.

Please feel free to contact me with any feedback on this revision guide so that later editions can continue to help students around the world. I can be contacted by email – either via OSC or Patrick_Roby@Hotmail.com

Pat Roby (Author)

Contents

Topic 1   Physics and Physical Measurement   3

Topic 2   Mechanics   7

Topic 3   Thermal Physics   20

Topic 4   Oscillations and Waves   30

Topic 5   Electric Circuits   52

Topic 6   Forces and Fields   65

Topic 7   Atomic and Nuclear Physics   76

Topic 8   Energy, Power and Climate Change   89

               Solutions to SL Section Problems   109

Topic 9   Motion in Fields   128

Topic 10   Thermal Physics (Thermodynamics)   142

Topic 11   Waves Phenomena   150

Topic 12   Electromagnetic Induction   165

Topic 13   Quantum Physics and Nuclear Physics   177

Topic 14   Digital Technology   191

               Solutions to HL Section Problems   197

Topic One: Physics and Physical Measurement

Orders of Magnitude

In the physical world, many quantities are too large or too small to write down on a piece of paper using the "normal" number system. We therefore commonly use scientific notation in Physics. It is sometimes useful to get an idea of the approximate size of a quantity without needing to know the exact number. For this, we can use a concept known as "order of magnitude". The order of magnitude of a quantity is simply the power of 10 in the scientific form notation. We either state quantities "to the nearest order of magnitude" – ie. to the nearest power of 10 – or we express ratios of quantities as differences of orders of magnitude.

Worked example:

(a) State the (rest) mass of an electron to the nearest order of magnitude (get data from data book or text)

(b) State the ratio of the rest mass a proton to that of an electron as a difference of orders of magnitude

Solutions

(a) the mass of an electron to the nearest order of magnitude is 10^{-30} kg (mass = 9.11×10^{-31} kg – this rounds to 1×10^{-30} kg or simply 10^{-30} kg)

(b) $\dfrac{m_p}{m_e} = \dfrac{1.673 \times 10^{-27}}{9.11 \times 10^{-31}} = 1.8 \times 10^4 \approx 10^4$

Quantities

A physical quantity has a unit and a magnitude. The unit describes the nature of the quantity and the magnitude, the size. Some quantities, called vector quantities, also have direction (those for which direction has no meaning are called scalar quantities). Certain units are defined by quantities that exist in reality and remain constant. Such units are called fundamental units. All units can be derived from fundamental units. Hence the set of all units comprise fundamental (or base) units and derived units. Fundamental units on their own are sufficient to define all quantities.

Common Quantities and their Units

Example T1.1 – complete the table

Quantity	Quantity Symbol	Unit Symbol	F/D	V/S
Mass				
Length				
Time				
Current				
Temperature				
Force				
Displacement				
Speed				
Acceleration				
Pressure				
Potential difference				
Resistance				
Energy				
Charge				
Velocity				
Power				
Frequency				

Fundamental or Derived

Vector or Scalar

Example T1.2

Show that the kilowatt hour (kWh) and the joule (J) are both derived from the same fundamental (or base) units

Prefixes

It is convenient to express very large or very small quantities using prefix multipliers. The common multipliers used are as follows:

Example T1.3 – complete the table

Name	Multiplication factor	Example -	conversion to S.I. units (using scientific notation)
nano (n)	10^{-9}	300nm =	
micro (μ)	10^{-6}	0.6 μs =	
milli (m)	10^{-3}	500 mV =	
centi (c)	10^{-2}	0.3 cm =	
kilo (k)	10^{3}	101 kPa =	
mega (M)	10^{6}	23.4 MN =	

Uncertainty and Error

A random uncertainty is an unpredictable and largely uncontrollable uncertainty. Examples include human reaction time and other forms of human measurement. Random uncertainties can be reduced by taking the average of repeated measurements.

A systematic error is an error that occurs on all measurements. An example is a zero error on a newton meter (spring balance). Systematic errors can often easily be detected on a graph of the measurements versus a related (dependent) variable – the whole curve, for example, will be this error distance too high – and will miss the origin when it should pass through it. Systematic errors are not reduced by taking repeated measurements.

Precision and Accuracy

An accurate instrument is one whose graduations correspond to the true quantities. For example the 1m mark on a ruler corresponds correctly (accurately) to a length of 1 metre, if the ruler is accurate.

The maximum uncertainty in reading an instrument is generally taken to be half a division on the graduation of the instrument. For example, if a metre ruler has 1mm graduations, the maximum uncertainty in recording a length is 0.5mm

A precise instrument is one that has a very fine graduation – so it records measurements to within a very small uncertainty. For example, a ruler with 1mm graduations is less precise than a ruler with 0.5mm graduations (but it may be more, or less, accurate)

Calculation of Uncertainties

If quantities are multiplied together (e.g. F = ma) or divided (e.g. speed = distance/time) then the percentage (or fractional) error of the product (e.g. of F) is obtained by adding the percentage (or fractional) errors of the individual errors,

If quantities are added or subtracted (e.g. perimeter = length + length + width + width) then the absolute (actual) error is obtained by adding the absolute error for each measurement.

Significant Figures

In Physics, numbers representing quantities have implied uncertainties. The uncertainty corresponds to half the next significant digit on the number. For example, $45 \text{ N} \Rightarrow 45 \pm 0.5 \text{ N}$. $45.67 \text{ N} \Rightarrow 45.67 \pm 0.005 \text{ N}$

Vector Quantities

A vector quantity is a quantity that has both size (magnitude) and direction. In Physics, vector quantities are represented using arrows. The length of the arrow represents the magnitude of the quantity and the direction of the arrow, the direction of the quantity. Solving vector problems can then be done either using mathematical geometry or scale diagrams.

Unlike scalars, which are just treated like numbers when added, direction must be taken into account when adding vector quantities. They are added by summing head-to-tail vectors, then either by direct measurement of scale drawing or by using geometry. The vectors are drawn, in any order, the head of one joining the tail of the next. The resultant vector is the vector that joins the tail (start) of the first vector to the head (end) of the last vector. Any vector can be considered as a sum of several vectors. It is common and useful to consider single vectors as two perpendicular vectors. These are called component vectors. The process of splitting a vector into two perpendicular components is called resolution (vector has been resolved). The process of combining two or more vectors into a single vector is called vector summation (finding the resultant vector).

Example T1.4

(a) A 5kg mass has forces acting on it as shown in the diagram. By scale diagram, or otherwise, find the resultant force acting on the mass:

Note: The diagram is not drawn to scale
The 3N force is perpendicular to the 4N force
The 7N force is at 45° to the 4N force

(b) Resolve the weight of a 25kg mass on a slope at 30° to horizontal into components parallel and perpendicular to the slope.

(c) Find the resultant speed of a man walking due East at 1.3 m/s across a flat lorry trailer if the lorry is moving due north at 3.2 m/s

Topic Two – Mechanics

Motion

The motion of an object is usually defined using three measurements: displacement, velocity and acceleration.

Less informative/useful quantities about motion are speed and distance travelled. These quantities are defined at certain points in time.

distance travelled - length of path taken

displacement - the position of an object relative to a defined starting position. This is described by giving the distance and direction from the starting point.

speed - rate at which distance is covered/changes (with time)

velocity - rate at which displacement changes (with time)

velocity is also referred to as "instantaneous velocity" since it is a measurement at an instant in time, rather than over a period of time. The velocity of an object is always the same as the speed, but direction of motion must also be included.

acceleration - rate at which velocity changes (with time)

Strictly, direction of acceleration should also be given – and in linear motion + represents velocity increasing in the "forwards" direction and − represents velocity increasing in the "reverse" direction.

average speed $= \dfrac{total\ distance\ travelled}{total\ time\ taken}$

Average speed can also be thought of as the constant speed in the given time to cover the same distance in question in that time.

average velocity $= \dfrac{total\ displacement}{total\ time\ taken}$

Average velocity can also be thought of as the constant velocity in a given time to cover the same displacement in question in that time.

relative velocity - the velocity of one object as seen from another

Relative velocity of A as seen from B = $V_A - V_B$ where V_A and V_B are the velocities of A and B

Example T2.1

A particle moves at constant speed in a anticlockwise semicircle, radius 12m, taking 3.5 seconds to travel to a point due north of the starting point.

    (a) find the average speed
    (b) find the average velocity
    (c) find the speed and velocity after 1 second
    (d) is the object accelerating?

Interpreting Motion Graphically

Graphs provide a very powerful way of describing any type of motion, whether it be uniformly accelerated, starting-and-stopping, or whatever.

In all cases:

- The gradient of a displacement versus time graph at any point in time gives the velocity of the object
- The gradient of a velocity versus time graph at any point in time gives the acceleration of the object
- The area under a velocity versus time graph from one point in time to another gives the displacement of the of the object at the second point relative to the first (it is often more useful to find area from t=0 to any particular point in time – to give displacement from starting point)

These simple rules lead to the derivation of the equations of motion (done later).

Example T2.2

The graphs below (labelled A to O) give information about the motion of 15 different objects. t represents time, s represents displacement, v; velocity and a, acceleration. Use the graphs to answer the question that follows.

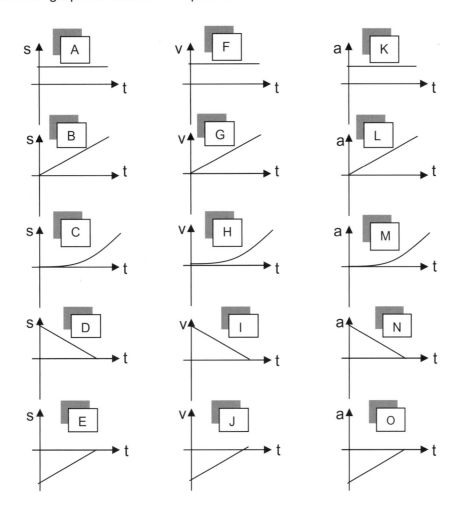

Complete the table below by inserting 0 or $+$ or $-$ in the sign columns – to show the sign of the displacement, velocity or acceleration throughout the time on the graph and inc (for increasing) or dec (for decreasing) or con (for constant) in the change columns, to show how displacement, velocity or acceleration change as time elapses.

(for the velocity graphs (F-J), assume that the object starts (when t=0) at zero displacement and for the acceleration graphs (K-O), assume that the object starts at zero displacement and velocity)

graph	displacement		velocity		acceleration	
	sign	change	sign	change	sign	change
A						
B						
C						
D						
E						
F						
G						
H						
I						
J						
K						
L						
M						
N						
O						

Equations of Motion – Derivation

These equations apply only to motion that is uniformly accelerated.

Consider a general example of such motion

initial velocity (at time t = 0) = u
final velocity (at time t = t) = v
acceleration = a (constant, over all time)
displacement = s

The velocity versus time graph for such motion would look as in the diagram on the right:

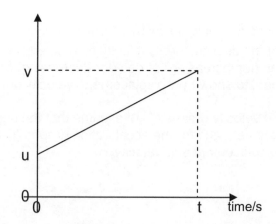

Derivation of Equations of Motion from graph

Example T2.3

Derive the equations of motion from the graph shown just previously

Hint: start by finding the gradient (slope) and noting that acceleration = slope, then find area (=displacement)

Falling Objects

When solving problems involving objects falling under the influence of the Earth's gravitational field, we usually assume:

- that the gravitational field strength, g, (which is equal to, and also called, acceleration due to gravity) is constant (and taken to be $9.81ms^{-2}$)
- that the weight of the object is the only force acting on it

If these two conditions do indeed apply it means that the acceleration of the object is constant and the object is said to be in free-fall

$$weight\,(F) = mg$$

$$F = ma \Rightarrow a = \frac{F}{m} = \frac{mg}{m} = g$$

so, for objects in free fall $a = g = 9.81ms^{-2}$ (on surface of Earth)

These conditions do not strictly apply in reality. The first condition is very close to true for objects very close to the surface of the Earth (within a few km, certainly). However the second condition ignores air resistance – a force whose magnitude (size) depends upon:

- the size, shape and texture of the surface
- the speed of the object

As the speed of an object increases the air resistance also increases until at a certain speed, the force of air resistance is equal to the weight of the object, the resultant force is then zero and so the object no longer accelerates. The constant speed reached is called terminal speed or terminal velocity.

Example T2.4

A stone is projected vertically into the air, from the ground, at 25 ms^{-1}.
(a) Find the maximum height reached
(b) Find the total time taken to hit the ground.

Example T2.5

If an iron ball and a plastic ball are dropped in air from the same height, explain what would be observed and whether the equations of motion would be useful in each case

Forces

Some Examples of Forces (list is not exhaustive)

normal reaction (contact force)
applied force
friction (between solid surfaces)
air or fluid resistance (also called drag) (between solids and liquids or gases)
electric/magnetic/gravitational
weight (often loosely called gravity)
tension

Free body diagrams

A free body diagram shows all the forces acting on the body (and NOT the resultant force). The resultant force acting on the body is thus the vector sum of all these forces.

Examples T2.6

Draw free body diagrams for the following, showing relative size, direction and names of forces.

1) A woman standing on the floor

2) A man falling through the air, ignore air resistance

3) A mass sliding down frictionless slope

4) A parachutist falling at terminal speed

Newton's First law

A body will continue in its current state of motion (velocity) unless acted on by a resultant force.

$$\text{i.e.: } a = 0 \ if \ sum \ of \ forces \ (resultant \ force), \sum F = 0$$

If it is known that the resultant force on an object is zero, we can therefore conclude that the acceleration of the object is zero. The converse is also often useful; if it is known that the acceleration is zero, we can conclude that the resultant force is zero.

Example T2.7

A 10 kg mass is on a slope elevated at 40° to the horizontal. The mass remains stationary.

    (a) Draw a free body diagram for the mass
    (b) Resolve the weight of the mass into components perpendicular to the slope
    (c) State the size and direction of the frictional force acting on the mass

We should note that zero acceleration does not imply that a body is motionless – only that its velocity (speed and direction) is constant (unchanging). However, if a body is (and remains) motionless this does imply that the resultant force acting on the body is zero. We need to be very careful here. If a body stops momentarily (for an instant), it can be in a state of acceleration (i.e. speeding up, in a certain direction) – in which case, the resultant force on the body is not zero.

Example T2.8

A 5 kg mass is thrown vertically into the air. The table below describes its state of motion immediately after it is thrown, half way up during its ascent, at the highest point, half way down during its descent and just before it hits the ground. Complete the table by writing + (positive), – (negative) or 0 (zero) to show the direction of displacement, velocity, acceleration and force at each stage. Take the ground level as zero displacement and take the upwards direction as positive direction.

Motion	Displacement	Velocity	Acceleration	Force
Immediately after thrown				
Half - way up				
At highest point				
Half - way down				
just before hits ground				

Equilibrium

A body is said to be in translational equilibrium if the vector sum of all the forces acting on the body is equal to zero. (Note that such a body may not be in rotational equilibrium – net *rotational* forces may also exist). Translational motion is motion from one place to another. If a body is **not** in translational equilibrium, the effect of the unbalanced forces will be to accelerate it from one place to another.

Newton's Second law

The acceleration of a body is proportional to the resultant force acting on the body (and is in the same direction)

i.e.: $\quad \sum F = ma \quad (\sum F$ = sum of forces or resultant force)

Example T2.9

If the slope in example T2.7 were frictionless, calculate the resultant force on the mass and acceleration of the mass, whilst on the slope.

An important follow-on from Newton's second law is that not only is the size of the acceleration proportional to the resultant force, but also that the direction of the acceleration is the same as the direction of the resultant force. To find the direction of acceleration, it is often useful to first find the direction of the resultant force – i.e. to deduce acceleration from force rather than from change in velocity (thinking about velocity and direction of motion often confuses direction of acceleration. For example, in Example T2.8, finding direction of acceleration is easy if you simply consider the direction of resultant force - weight)

Example T2.10

Mark on with arrows the direction of the acceleration of a mass oscillating on a spring (as shown in the diagram below) at positions A, B and C. The mass is shown at the highest position – position A. Position B is the position where the mass will eventually come to rest and position C is the lowest position of the mass.

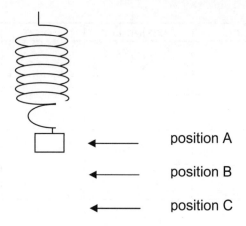

position A

position B

position C

Newton's third law of motion

When two particles interact, they always exert equal and opposite forces on each other.

Forces are therefore often described as (equal and opposite) pairs ("Newton's 3rd Law pairs"), since it is not possible to have an unpaired force.

Note that Newton 3rd Law pairs are always:

- ✓ equal to each other in size – so if one changes, the other must change also
- ✓ the same type of force (so if one is tension, so must the other be etc.)
- ✓ acting on two different objects - ie. not on the same object (since they are the forces on the two particles when the two particles interact) (so the weight of a brick and the normal reaction force acting on it, whilst equal and opposite, do not constitute a Newton's 3rd Law pair)

Example T2.11

Jessica attempts to lift a 500N weight off the ground by applying an upwards force of 300N to a string attached to the weight. Draw a free-body diagram of the weight and identify/describe all the (Newton's 3rd law) pairs of equal and opposite forces.

Momentum and Impulse

Defining Equations

momentum = mass x velocity   ($p = mv$)

impulse = change in momentum   ($Impulse = \Delta p = m\Delta v$)

note that momentum is a vector quantity, so a change in direction is a change in momentum

Units of impulse are usually written as Ns but can also be written as the same as units of momentum ie. $kgms^{-1}$ (read kilograms metres per second)

Link to force

$force = mass \times acceleration$ ($Newton's\ 2^{nd}\ law$)

$$= mass \times \frac{(v-u)}{t} \ \ where\ v = final\ velocity, u = initial\ velocity$$

$$= \frac{m(v-u)}{t} = \frac{mv-mu}{t} = \frac{change\ in\ momentum}{t}$$

$in\ symbols,\ F = \frac{\Delta p}{t} = \frac{impulse}{t}$ ($impulse = change\ in\ momentum, p = momentum$)

$\therefore Ft = impulse$ ($written\ Impulse = F\Delta t$)

Example T2.12

A road vehicle has a mass of 1.2 tonnes (1,200 kg) and is initially stationary. The engine imparts an impulse of 14.4kNs on the vehicle.

    (a) At what speed is the vehicle moving after the engine force has been applied?
    (b) If the acceleration of the vehicle was 0.8ms^{-2}, find the force exerted by the engine
    (c) Find the time taken for the vehicle to reach the speed calculated in part (a)

Impulse for non-constant forces

If force is not constant, the impulse (change in momentum) can be found in two possible ways. Either use impulse = average force x time or find the impulse from the area under a force versus time graph (but note that the force units must be newtons and the time must be seconds.

Conservation of momentum

In a closed system, the total momentum of all the masses in the system remains constant.

key points   - the total momentum of a closed system always remains constant (i.e. is conserved)
- if one object gains momentum, the other must gain an equal amount of momentum in the opposite direction (negating the gain of first object)

Types of collision

elastic   - kinetic energy is also conserved
- objects bounce without conversion of kinetic energy to other forms (speed of approach = speed of separation)

inelastic   - there is a maximum loss of kinetic energy
(but the momentum must still be conserved)
-    objects stick together on impact

partially   - there is some loss of kinetic energy, but objects do not
inelastic   stick together on impact
- momentum, as always, is still conserved

explosion   - like a collision, where momentum is conserved, but energy is converted from an external source (to cause the explosion) into kinetic energy. Objects move away from each other, rather than towards each other.

Example T2.13

Each example below (next page) shows two-body collisions. Complete the diagrams by drawing labelled velocity vectors (not to scale) on the bodies where they are incomplete. (Masses of objects are omitted on the right – they are the same as masses before collision!) By calculating the kinetic energy before and after each collision, indicate in each case whether the collision is elastic, inelastic or partially elastic.

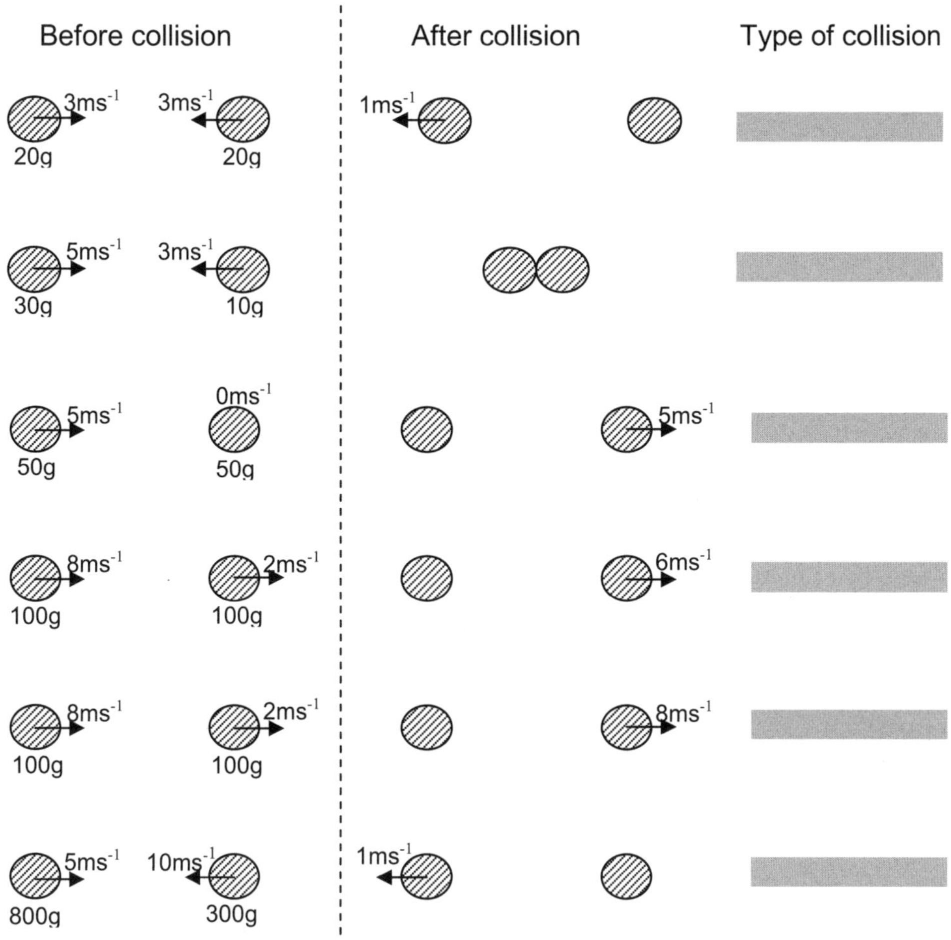
Before collision
After collision
Type of collision
3ms-1
3ms-1
20g
20g
1ms-1
5ms-1
3ms-1
30g
10g
5ms-1
0ms-1
50g
50g
5ms-1
8ms-1
2ms-1
100g
100g
6ms-1
8ms-1
2ms-1
100g
100g
8ms-1
5ms-1
10ms-1
800g
300g
1ms-1

Work, Energy, Power

Key Point: - Energy is never gained or lost, only converted from one form to another

Quantifying types of energy:

Kinetic ("movement" energy): $E_k = \frac{1}{2}mv^2$

where $m = mass, v = velocity$

work done (energy converted by the "force provider"): $W = Fd$

where $F = force\ applied,\ d = distance\ moved\ in\ direction\ of\ force$

Note that work done can also be found by finding the area under a force (N) versus distance (s) graph – and is particularly useful when force is variable

Heat (energy emitted or absorbed): $Q = mc\Delta T$

where $m = mass, c = specific\ heat\ capacity, \Delta T = temperature\ change$

Electric (energy used or converted): $E = VIt = Vq$

where $V = potential\ difference, I = current, t = time, q = $ charge

Latent Heat (thermal energy absorbed or released) : $Q = ml$

where $m = mass, l = specific\ latent\ heat\ of\ fusion\,/\,vaporization$

Gravitational (increase in energy due to height): $\Delta E_p = mg\Delta h$

where $m = mass, g = gravity, \Delta h = change\ in\ height$

Other useful equations

Work done = energy converted

Power = work done / time taken

$$Efficiency\ (\%) = \frac{useful\ work\ done}{total\ energy\ used} \times 100$$

Example T2.14

A 2kW electric motor is used to run a water pump and in 3 hours pumps approximately 100 tonnes (1 tonne=1000kg) of water, lifting the water into a canal 5m higher.

  (a) Find the work done by the pump in this time
  (b) Find the potential energy gained by the water in this time
  (c) Calculate the efficiency of the pump and explain how the principal of conservation of energy applies in this example.

Example T2.15

A man of mass 90 kg walks along a horizontal road, covering a distance of 3 km. Find the work done by the man in covering this distance.

Non Uniformly Accelerated Motion

For the purposes of this course there are two instances to deal with concerning non-uniformly accelerated motion.

  ✓ recognizing deviations from constant acceleration (in real situations). For example, recognizing that objects falling in air do not really accelerate at a uniform rate – air resistance, a non-uniform force, affects the motion
  ✓ circular motion

Circular Motion

We consider only uniform circular motion – that is: motion of objects moving in a circle at a constant (uniform) speed.

For such motion:

- the acceleration is always directed towards the centre of the circle
- the acceleration is called centripetal acceleration
- the resultant force on the object must be towards the centre of the circle
- this resultant force is called centripetal force
- to describe circular motion there must be a centripetal force acting on the object
- the size of the acceleration depends on the speed of the object and on the radius of the circle described by the object, thus the centripetal acceleration on an object describing uniform circular motion is given by:

  $a = \dfrac{v^2}{r}$ where v is the speed and r is the radius

- the size of the centripetal force required depends also on the size of the mass. As usual, $F = ma$ Hence the centripetal force required to maintain the uniform circular motion of such an object is given by:

  $F = ma = m\dfrac{v^2}{r}$ or $F = \dfrac{mv^2}{r}$

Example T2.16

A string is used to twirl a 300g mass in a horizontal circle of radius 25 cm, in zero gravity conditions, so that the mass moves at a speed of 2 ms^{-1}

(a) find the tension in the string

(b) if the mass is now twirled in a vertical circle **with gravity** at the same speed, draw a free body diagram showing the mass at the lowest point and calculate the tension in the string at this point.

Note

This example illustrates the point that centripetal force is the required resultant force that must act on a mass if the mass is to describe a circle. This resultant force can be from a single force or the result of two or more forces.

Topic 3 – Thermal Physics

Temperature and Thermal Energy

Temperature

Temperature is the degree of hotness of a substance. On a microscopic level, temperature is a measure of the average kinetic energy of the particles within a substance.

We can therefore say that if a substance is hotter then each particle will (on average) have a greater kinetic energy (so gas particles will be moving – or vibrating – faster)

This kinetic energy can be vibrational motion, in the case of solids, or translational motion, in the case of liquids or gases.

Thermal contact

Two objects are said to be in thermal contact if it is possible for thermal energy to be transferred directly from one object to the other as a result of the **temperature difference** between the two objects.

Heat (Thermal Energy)

Thermal energy is often also called heat energy.

If two objects are in thermal contact, thermal energy will transfer from one to the other, and vice versa. Thermal energy ("heat") is thus the energy transfer that results when two objects are in thermal contact with each other and one is hotter (at a higher temperature than) the other.

Thermal Equilibrium

The net, (overall) transfer of thermal energy is always from the object with the highest temperature to the object with the lowest temperature. Therefore the hottest object will cool down and the coolest object will warm up until they both reach the same temperature. At this point the two objects are said to be in thermal equilibrium.

If two objects are in thermal contact and they are both at the same temperature, it does not mean that no thermal energy is being transferred from one object to the other, but that there is no overall transfer of energy. For this to be the situation, it must be that thermal energy is flowing equally in both directions. This situation is described as thermal equilibrium. So objects in thermal contact and at the same temperature are said to be in thermal equilibrium.

Temperature Scales

The two common temperature scales are the celsius temperature scale and the kelvin temperature scale.

The kelvin scale is also referred as the absolute temperature scale.

The absolute (kelvin) temperature scale starts at the lowest possible temperature – zero kelvin (0 K – degrees word and sign is omitted).

This equates to a temperature of −273 °C. Since an increment of 1°C is the same as an increment of 1 K, converting from °C to K or visa versa is very easy.

To convert from °C to K: Add   273
To convert from K to °C: Subtract   273

Examples:
0 K	=	−273 °C
0 °C	=	273 K
100 °C	=	373 K
150 K	=	−123 °C

Internal Energy

Internal Energy = Potential Energy + Kinetic Energy

The potential energy of a substance increases if the attractive bonds between the atoms are weakened (by increasing the average distance between adjacent molecules)

The kinetic energy of a substance increases if the motion (translational or vibrational) is increased

Increasing the temperature of a substance is effected by increasing the average kinetic energy of the molecules

Changing the state of a substance (from solid to liquid or liquid to gas) is effected by increasing the potential energy of the molecules

Adding energy to a substance (by heating it or doing work on it) can result in one of the following:

- The temperature can increase (KE increases)
- The state can change (PE increases)
- Energy can be lost by the substance at an equal rate (equilibrium is said to occur)
- The substance can chemically change (e.g. burn, decompose)

Key point: Temperature of a substance is a measure of the average kinetic energy of molecules in that substance

The rate (°C per second) at which the **temperature** changes depends on:

- The rate at which net energy is added
- The mass of substance
- The specific heat capacity of the substance

The rate (kg per second) at which the **state** changes depends on:

- The rate at which net energy is added
- The specific latent heat of fusion/vaporization of the substance

Thermal Energy Transfer

To understand thermal energy transfer it is best to think of thermal energy as "molecular motion" (vibrational or translational)
Thermal energy (heat energy) is transferred from one place to another by three ways:

1. Conduction – thermal energy (vibrations) is passed on by molecules colliding with their neighbouring molecules – neighbouring molecules therefore move more, increasing their thermal energy, and so on
2. Convection – thermal energy is moved simply by molecules containing thermal energy moving
3. Radiation – thermal energy is transferred from a "hot" body by infra-red (heat) radiation. This radiation can then be absorbed by another body, whose internal energy would then increase.

Some characteristics of thermal energy transfer

*   The only type of heat transfer in solids is conduction
    The main type of heat transfer in liquids and gases is convection
*   Radiation is most effective when there are no particles in the way – i.e. in a vacuum
*   Conduction and convection require matter
*   Heat transfer by convection is usually in the upwards direction, since hotter particles move more, take up more space and make that part of the fluid (liquid or gas) less dense
*   All objects radiate heat – the hotter, the greater the amount of radiation
*   Conduction can and does take place in fluids, although generally only to a minor extent since the particles are not in close proximity to each other, as in solids.
*   Metals are good conductors of heat, since they contain free electrons that assist the passage of heat through the substance
*   Non-metals are classed as thermal insulators
*   Good conductors that are hot *feel* hot to touch because they quickly transfer heat to the contact point, whilst hot insulators don't feel so hot – the contact point cools on contact and the thermal energy is not quickly replaced. (the same applies to cold objects)

Temperature, internal energy and thermal energy (heat) – differences explained:

Temperature is a measure of the average kinetic energy of a substance.
The internal energy of a substance is the total kinetic and potential energy of the substance
Thermal energy (heat) is the energy transfer that results when a high temperature body is placed in thermal contact with a low temperature body.
It is incorrect to talk about the thermal energy of a substance, as it is incorrect to talk about temperature transfer.

Amount of Substance (The mole)

Gas pressure does not depend on mass of particles, but rather, the number of particles of a given gas. For example 1000 molecules per cubic metre of hydrogen gas at room temperature will exert the same pressure as 1000 molecules per cubic metre of oxygen molecules – even though oxygen molecules are 16 times more massive than hydrogen molecules.

The above example uses simple, but unrealistic numbers. At room temperature and pressure, one cubic metre will contain about 2.5×10^{25} molecules! We use a more convenient unit to measure "number of particles" – the mole.

The mole is thus defined as An amount of substance such that it contains the same number of molecules as there atoms in exactly 12g of carbon-12

Avogadro Constant

This number is called the Avogadro constant, N_A, where
$N_A = 6.02 \times 10^{23} \, mol^{-1}$

Molar mass

The molar mass of a substance is the mass of one mole of a particular substance. Molar masses of elements can easily found on the periodic table. For example, the molar mass of helium gas (consists of helium atoms) is 4g and the molar mass of oxygen gas (consists of O_2 molecules) is 16g x 2 = 32g

Thermal Properties of Matter

Specific Heat Capacity

The energy required to increase the temperature of 1 kilogram of a substance by 1 °C varies from one substance to another. This property is known as the specific heat capacity of the substance.

Equation:
$$c = \frac{Q}{m \times \Delta T}$$

c=specific heat capacity

Q=energy required / released as a consequence of temperature change (joules)

m=mass of substance (kilograms)

ΔT =temperature change(°C)

Example T3.1

27 KJ of energy is needed to warm up 3 kg of a substance by 12 °C.
Find its specific heat capacity.

Example T3.2

When 500 grams of water cools down by 5°C it is found that approximately 10.5kJ of energy is given out – heating the cooler surroundings. Find an approximate value for the specific heat capacity of water

Example T3.3

Ice has a specific heat capacity of $2100 \, Jkg^{-1}{}^{\circ}C^{-1}$. How much energy is needed to increase the temperature of a block of ice with a mass of 7.5kg from –18°C to –5°C?

Variation in Specific Heat Capacity

Different substances have different specific heat capacities because, per kilogram, they contain different numbers of molecules and because the chemical (bonding) properties are different for different substances

Water has an extremely high specific heat capacity. This makes it a very useful substance for cooling systems for car engines and other machinery. One kilogram of water will absorb a lot of energy whilst only increasing by a small temperature. (4200 J for 1 kg to increase by 1°C)

Heat Capacity (Thermal Capacity)

Specific heat capacity relates to **substances**. *Heat capacity* relates to **objects**.

The heat capacity (thermal capacity) of an object is the energy needed to increase the temperature of the object by 1°C. (This quantity is not as useful as specific heat capacity)

Equation: $\qquad C = \dfrac{Q}{\Delta T}$

$C = heat \; capacity$

$Q = energy \; required / released \; as \; a \; consequence \; of \; temperature \; change \; (joules)$

$\Delta T = temperature \; change \, ({}^{\circ}C)$

Example T3.4

A wood-burning stove (fire) is used to heat up a room. The oven, which has a mass of 220kg, requires 1.66 MJ of heat energy for it to warm up, on a cold morning, from 9°C to 21°C.

- (a) Find the heat capacity of the oven
- (b) Assuming that the oven is made of only one material, find the specific heat capacity of this material.

Change of state/phase

solid $\leftrightarrow$ *liquid*

$$\left(\begin{array}{l} solid \rightarrow liquid = "melting" \\ liquid \rightarrow solid = "freezing" \; or \; "solidification" \; or \; "fusion" \end{array} \right)$$

Energy is required to change the state, or phase, of a substance from a solid to a liquid, and energy is released when a substance changes from a liquid to a solid. The energy needed to melt one kilogram of a substance is equal to the energy released when one kilogram of the same substance, in its liquid phase, freezes at constant temperature.

This energy is known as the latent heat of fusion. (Fusion is another word for freezing)

Equation $Q = ml$

$Q = energy\ needed\ to\ melt\ the\ substance$

$(or\ energy\ released\ when\ substance\ freezes)$

$m = mass\ of\ substance\ changing\ state$

$l = specific\ latent\ heat\ of\ fusion$

Example T3.5

An electrical heater is used to melt 5 Kg of ice, which has already been warmed up to its melting point (0°C). It is found that 1.7 MJ is needed. Find the specific latent heat of fusion of water using this information.

$liquid \rightarrow gas\ (vapour)$ $\left(\begin{array}{l} liquid \rightarrow gas = "vaporisation" \\ gas \rightarrow liquid = "condensation" \end{array}\right)$

Energy is required to change the state, or phase, of a substance from a liquid to a gas, and energy is released when a substance changes from a gas to a liquid The energy needed to vaporize one kilogram of a substance is equal to the energy released when one kilogram of the same substance, in its gas phase, condenses.

This energy is known as the latent heat of vaporization.

Equation: $Q = ml$

$Q = energy\ needed\ to\ vaporize\ the\ substance$

$(or\ energy\ released\ when\ substance\ condenses)$

$m = mass\ of\ substance\ changing\ state$

$l = specific\ latent\ heat\ of\ vaporization$

Example T3.6

Given that the latent heat of vaporization of water is 2.26×10^6 Jkg^{-1} how much energy is needed to vaporize 500 grams of water?

Molecular Structure of the Phases

Solid substances contain atoms or molecules that are fixed in one place. The particles do not move from one place to another (translate), but vibrate. Particles are fixed in place because of the attractive forces holding them together. The (vibrational) motion of the particles gives them their kinetic energy. The position of the particles, in an attractive field, gives the particles their potential energy (which is negative).

Liquid substances contain atoms or molecules that are able to move, but are still attracted to each other. The kinetic energy of the particles is now attributable to their translational motion. Motion is impeded by attractive forces between particles and by particle collisions. Since the particles are still in an attractive field, they still have potential energy (which is negative, but closer to zero than in solids).

Gaseous substances contain atoms or molecules that are completely separated and move around quickly, in straight lines until they collide with each other or an object and then they bounce. The kinetic energy of these particles is high because of their very high speeds (translational motion). Forces between particles are negligible (effectively zero), so the potential energy of a gas is usually assumed to be zero (unless under very high pressure, or very low temperature).

Heating a Substance through its phase changes

At this level, for calculations, we generally assume:
- that a solid must be heated to its melting/freezing point before it begins to melt
- that the solid substance at its melting/freezing point completely melts before any of it increases in temperature
- that the melted, now liquid, substance must be heated to its boiling point before it begins to vaporize
- that the boiling liquid then continues to vaporize as more energy is added
- (it is then possible to heat up the vapour above the boiling point, but this is uncommon in practice since the vapour leaves the container and moves away from the heat source)

The energy changes occurring are as follows:

Increasing the temperature of the solid:

Energy needed $= mc\Delta T$
This energy results in an increase in the kinetic energy of the particles
The greater average separation of the particles means that there is also a slight increase in their potential energy

Changing the state of the solid (at melting point) into a liquid (at same temperature)

Energy needed $= ml$ (l is specific latent heat of fusion)
This results in an increase in the potential energy of the particles to a point where the attractive forces are weak enough to allow translational movement of the particles.

Increasing the temperature of the liquid:

Energy needed $= mc\Delta T$ (note that the value for c is different to the solid substance)
This energy results in an increase in the kinetic energy of the particles
The greater average separation of the particles means that there is also a slight increase in their potential energy

Changing the state of the liquid (at boiling point) into a gas (at same temperature)

Energy needed $= ml$ (l is specific latent heat of vaporization)
This results in an increase in the potential energy of the particles to a point where there are no longer attractive forces between them. The potential energy of the particles is now zero.

If the vapour (gas) is heated further, the particles move faster, their kinetic energies are increased and the temperature continues to increase.

Evaporation of a liquid below its boiling point

A liquid will evaporate at temperatures below its boiling point – for example a puddle evaporates without boiling.
The particles that escape from the liquid are those closest to the surface. They have to first gain kinetic energy, which is then converted into potential energy (as they separate from other particles). Once their potential energy has been increased to zero (and they no longer attract each other) they escape. The energy comes from either the surroundings, above the liquid, or from the particles below, or both. Particles below the surface transfer energy to the particles on the surface by colliding with them. If the surface particles gain enough speed from one or more such collisions they will escape.

The rate of evaporation of a liquid depends upon:
- The temperature of the liquid
- The temperature of the surroundings
- The amount of vapour already in the surroundings (if the gas above the liquid is saturated with vapour, no further **net** evaporation can take place – equilibriumis reached – rate of evaportaion = rate of condensation)
- The surface area of the liquid
- The nature of the liquid (volatility of liquid)

Evaporation and Boiling – differences

A liquid evaporates continually, even at low temperatures. Surface molecules gain sufficient energy from the bulk of the liquid to become gas molecules.

A liquid boils at a certain temperature (which depends on the external air pressure and on the substance). When this happens, molecules within the bulk of the liquid (not just at the surface) gain sufficient energy from surrounding molecules to become gas molecules, and hence form bubbles.

Water can be made to boil at quite low temperatures by decreasing air pressure (e.g. at top of mountains). Conversely, water boils at a higher temperature when external pressure is increased (e.g. pressure cookers)

Kinetic Model of an Ideal Gas

The kinetic model of an ideal gas is a model that explains the macroscopic (bulk) properties of a gas, like temperature, pressure and volume.

The assumptions of the model are:

Molecules are point molecules – they occupy no space
Molecules have random motion – so they tend to spread out evenly in a container
Collisions between pairs of molecules and between the walls of the container are elastic – so that the total kinetic energy of a gas left undisturbed will remain constant

These assumptions apply to an "ideal gas" – one that behaves perfectly. In reality, under normal conditions of temperature and pressure, gases do approximate closely to these assumptions and behave in a very similar way to an ideal gas.

Pressure

We can explain how pressure arises on the walls of a container filled with gas by considering each gas particle as an elastic ball, perhaps like a billiard ball.
To keep numbers simple, imagine such a ball has a mass of 1kg and is travelling at a speed of 5ms^{-1} towards a wall. The diagram below shows the arrangement:

As the ball hits the wall its momentum must be rapidly changed (from 5kgms^{-1} to –5kgms^{-1} in the example on the right). A force is required to do this. The force is provided by the wall. Newton's Third Law also applies here – the ball applies a force on the wall, and the wall applies a force on the ball.

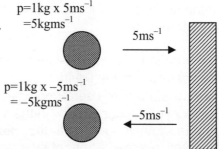

If we assume that the time between collisions is 0.2 seconds – so that each collision takes, on average 0.2 seconds, then we could find the average force of this particle exerted on the container walls by as follows:

$$F = \frac{\Delta p}{\Delta t} = \frac{(-5-5)}{0.2} = -50N \quad \text{(ignoring the minus, 50N)}$$

This is the way that kinetic theory assumes gases to behave – ie. that gases are made up of many tiny spheres, each of which behaves as has just been described.

Pressure - Definition

Pressure is defined to be force per unit area ($P = \dfrac{F}{A}$) so it can be explained by the average force of all collisions, such as the one described above, acting over the surface area of the inside of the container.

Using this model it is easy to see that pressure is increased by:

- increasing the speed of the particles
- increasing the mass of the particles
- decreasing the area of the collision surface, by decreasing the volume of the gas (whilst maintaining the number of particles).

It also explains that for a fixed mass of (an ideal) gas:

Increasing volume at constant temperature	$\Rightarrow$	pressure decreases
Increasing temperature at constant volume	$\Rightarrow$	pressure increases
Increasing temperature at constant pressure	$\Rightarrow$	volume increases

Temperature

Temperature is a measure of the average kinetic energy of the molecules of an ideal gas.

This means that if gas molecules are made to increase in speed, the gas will increase in temperature.

Thus, if a syringe of gas is reduced in volume by pushing in the plunger, we can explain its temperature increase by the fact that the gas molecules will collide with the now moving container wall and will rebound at a faster speed that its speed of approach. Since it gains speed, it has increased in kinetic energy and the temperature of the gas will increase. The temperature increase can also be explained directly in terms of energy arguments: work is done on the gas (a force is applied through a distance) and so the gas must have gained energy.

Topic 4 – Oscillations and Waves

Introduction

This topic is concerned with the nature and application of waves.
Waves are one means by which energy is transferred from one place to another.
Although a wave is defined as a transfer of energy, not matter, wave-transfer always involves oscillations – and these oscillations can be oscillations of an electromagnetic field (in the case of electromagnetic radiation (EMR) waves, such as light, x-rays etc. or oscillations of particles, such as water waves and sound waves.

In this guide, we shall refer to the oscillations in waves as "particle" oscillations – but must recognise that they can be particle or field oscillations.

Examples of oscillations

A mass bouncing up and down on a spring
A girl bouncing on a trampoline
A teacher pacing back and forth across the room
A child swinging on a playground swing
The air molecules as a sound wave passes
The molecules in any solid material

Simple Harmonic Motion (SHM)

Simple harmonic motion is a type of motion that accurately describes the oscillating motion of the "particles" in a wave.

It is important to realise that SHM is not merely oscillating motion: it is a specific kind of oscillating motion. Not all the examples of oscillations listed above are described by SHM

SHM involves motion where the acceleration of the particle is always proportional to and in the opposite direction to the displacement of the particle

The first, fourth and fifth examples on the list above are common examples of SHM

All waves involve SHM oscillations

An easy way to visualise SHM is to consider a pendulum.
Pendulum bobs swing with SHM

The central position of the bob (where it hangs when left to stop) is the equilibrium (zero displacement) position.

When the pendulum is set in motion, as it swings outwards its displacement increases, its velocity decreases and the force pulling it back to the centre increases.

This force tells us that the acceleration is always acting towards the centre.

The motion of particles in a wave is exactly the same. A cork on the surface of a water wave moves up and down (showing direction of "particles" the same way that a pendulum bob swings back and forth.

Some Terms to understand / learn

oscillation

- the term used to describe the movement of a "particle" (can also be field) from a position "to and fro" back to its original position. Vibration is an alternative term.

medium

- the "material" through which a wave travels (can also be a vacuum, for light and other forms of electro-magnetic radiation)

displacement

- the distance of a particle from its undisturbed (equilibrium) position
- usually determined by y axis position on wave graph/diagram
- measured in metres (but not normally stated or calculated)

amplitude

- the maximum displacement of a particle from equilibrium position
- represented by height (from middle/equilibrium position) of wave diagram
- measured in metres, although not a normally useful measurement

period

- the time taken for one complete oscillation of a particle ie. time taken for production of one complete wave
- measured in seconds
- symbol for period is T

frequency

- the number of waves/oscillations produced/observed per second
- measured in hertz
- symbol for frequency is f
- note that f=1/T

Phase difference

- The phase difference between two particles along a wave is the fraction of a cycle by which one moves behind the other
- The phase difference between two sources is the fraction of a cycle by which one
- source moves behind the other
- One cycle corresponds to 2π radians or 360°

Defining Simple Harmonic Motion

SHM is defined as motion where the acceleration of the particle is proportional to but in the opposite direction to the displacement of the particle.

i.e. $a \propto -x$ where: $a = acceleration$, $x = displacement$

The defining equation for simple harmonic motion is as follows:

$a = -\omega^2 x$ where: ω is the angular frequency of the oscillating particles

You must learn this equation; it is not given in the data booklet.

Further equations for the motion of particle describing SHM

(given in data booklet, but you must understand and know how to apply)

$x = x_0 \sin \omega t;$ $x = x_0 \cos \omega t$

$v = v_0 \cos \omega t;$ $v = -v_0 \sin \omega t$

$v = \pm \omega \sqrt{\left(x_0^2 - x^2\right)}$

$\omega = \dfrac{2\pi}{T}$

where

$x = displacement\ of\ particles\ at\ time\ t$

$x_0 = maximum\ displacement\ (amplitude)$

$v = velocity\ of\ particles\ at\ time\ t$

$v_0 = maximum\ velocity$

$\omega = angular\ frequency$

Angular frequency

The angular frequency of an oscillating particle is very similar to the frequency – but frequency gives oscillations per second and angular frequency gives angle per second (radians per second – $rads^{-1}$)

Remember, $360° = 2\pi$ radians

$frequency = 1 Hz \Rightarrow angular\ frequency = 2\pi rads^{-1}$

Hence: $frequency = 25 Hz \Rightarrow angular\ frequency = 50\pi rads^{-1}$

$T = 0.1s \Rightarrow f = \dfrac{1}{0.1} Hz = 10 Hz,\ \omega = \dfrac{2\pi}{0.1} rads^{-1} = 20\pi rads^{-1}$

Example T4.1

A pendulum is set in motion so that it swings back and forth, from A through B to C, then back through B to A and so on, as shown in the diagram shown below. Other information is given on the diagram.
We shall assume that it does not lose any energy as it swings, so it keeps swinging to equal amplitudes.

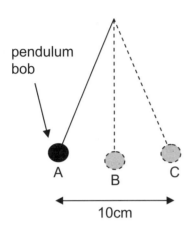

pendulum
bob

A   B   C

10cm

The pendulum bob is timed and it takes 1.25 seconds to move from
A→B→C→
B→A→B→C→B→A→B→C, so that it has moved a total distance of 50cm in this time.

As shown, the "swing distance" is 10cm

Take rightwards as the positive direction

(a) What is the amplitude of the motion of the bob? $5\ cm \Rightarrow 0.05\ m$
(b) What is the period of the motion? $0.25\ s$
(c) What is the angular frequency (ω) of the (motion of the) bob?
(d) What is the maximum velocity of the bob?
(e) Find the displacement, velocity and acceleration of the bob 0.125s after release
(f) Find the displacement, velocity and acceleration of the bob 0.25s after release
(g) Find the displacement, velocity and acceleration 0.375s after release
(h) Find the displacement, velocity and acceleration 0.6s after release

All the examples in example T4.1 could be applied, exactly the same way as a particle in a sound or water wave, or any other wave.

Example T4.2

The graph below shows how the velocity of a nitrogen molecule (in air), describing SHM, changes as a sound passes:

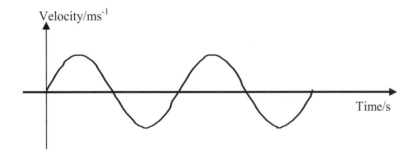

Velocity/ms^{-1}

Time/s

(a) Mark on the diagram with the letter A, positions where the displacement of the molecule is zero
(b) Mark on the diagram with the letter B, positions where the acceleration has maximum magnitude.
(c) Explain how the displacement can be found from the graph
(d) Explain how the acceleration can be found from the graph at any point in time
(e) Explain how the graph shows that the motion is (i) oscillating (ii) SHM
(f) Mark on the diagram with the letter C the point when the molecule has made one complete oscillation and explain how the displacement of the molecule can be found at this point in time. State this displacement.

Equations for the Kinetic Energy of a particle describing SHM

$$E_k = \frac{1}{2} m\omega^2 \left(x_0^{\;2} - x^2 \right)$$ where $E_k = kinetic\ energy\ when\ displacement\ is\ x$

$$E_{k(max)} = \frac{1}{2} m\omega^2 x_0^{\;2}$$ where $E_{k(max)} = maximum\ kinetic\ energy$

Example T4.3

Referring to the pendulum bob in example T4.1 and assuming that the bob has a mass of 30g:

(a) Describe how the energy changes (and the energy forms involved) as the bob swings back and forth (assume no energy loss due to heat/sound as a result of resistance to motion)
(b) Calculate the maximum kinetic energy of the bob
(c) Calculate the kinetic energy when its displacement is 3cm
(d) Calculate the kinetic energy of the bob when its displacement is $-2\,cm$
(e) Calculate the kinetic energy of the bob after 0.1s from time of release

Energy changes during SHM

The energy changes for SHM in general will always be an oscillation (variation) from kinetic energy to some other form. For the pendulum bob, for example it is KE→GPE→KE etc. (KE = kinetic energy, GPE = gravitational potential energy)
For a vibrating atom it would be KE→electrostatic potential energy→ KE etc. The electrostatic potential is, provided by the force of attraction between atoms.

Forced Oscillations and Resonance

Damping

In the above pendulum oscillation examples, we assumed no energy loss out of the "system" so that the system keeps oscillating forever. However in reality there will be energy losses as a result of resistive forces. **Damping is the process by which energy is removed** from an oscillating system. The result is that the amplitude of oscillation decreases with time until eventually the amplitude is zero and the oscillation has stopped completely.

Forces involved in damping are dissipative because they dissipate (remove) energy. It is logical that the forces always oppose the motion of the oscillating particle.

Examples of damping

- **Child on a swing** – air resistance and friction in the swing hinges are both damping forces (similar for pendulum)
- **Sound wave** – absorption of vibrations in surrounding materials (so energy transfer is sound → heat causing dissipation of sound (when you speak, the sound can carry – and can often be heard as an echo – but not forever))
- **Water wave** – wind forces and water resistance forces are both causes of wave amplitude decreasing. When a stone, for example, is dropped into a pond and ripples circulate outwards with decreasing amplitude and energy.

In most cases the transfer of energy out of a damped system is to heat energy (but can also be via sound energy or other forms) and this results in a slight temperature increase of the surroundings and of the system itself.

Extent of damping

Where there is no energy transfer out of a system the system is said to be undamped. Where energy transfer out of the system is small, damping is said to be light. An example would be a pendulum swinging in air. However, if the pendulum was placed in very thick oil or treacle it could take a long time just to fall to its equilibrium position (and not therefore actually oscillate). This is called heavy damping. If it is placed in oil thick enough to return quickly to its equilibrium position without oscillating, this is called critical damping.

Displacement / time graphs are shown below for these 4 situations.

Undamped oscillation (dotted lines show how amplitude varies)

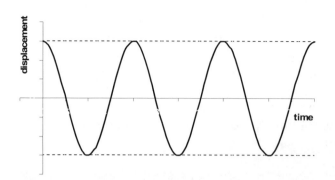

amplitude remains constant

Lightly damped oscillation (dotted lines show how amplitude varies)

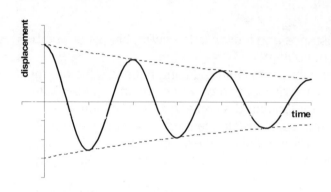

amplitude slowly decreases

Heavily damped oscillation

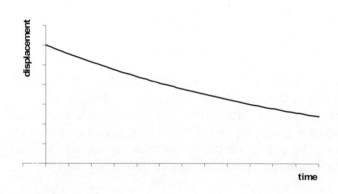

Particle no longer oscillates – amplitude line is same as actual displacement, which reduces gradually

Critically damped oscillation

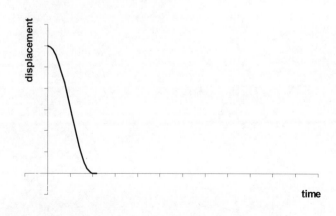

System is returned to equilibrium in shortest possible time and does not overshoot (into negative displacement and another oscillation) – again, amplitude line is same as actual displacement

Importance of damping

Sometimes it is necessary to dampen oscillating systems. A good example is a car on its suspension. If you push down hard on the front bonnet of a car, it will spring back up again. This is due to the suspension spring (shock absorber) which is necessary to absorb any sudden jolts when, for example, the car is driven rapidly over a bump. A shock absorber is an oscillating system that, when working correctly, has been critically damped. This critical damping is brought about by a cylinder of fluid inside the spring that is compressed. Without this fluid there would not be sufficient damping of the oscillating spring system and driving the car would be very dangerous. When going over a bump, for example, the car would be thrown into a bouncing motion. Part of the regular safety testing of motor cars involves checking that the suspension (shock absorber) system is correctly damped.

Summary:

Light damping – when the oscillations gradually die away
Heavy damping – when the system returns slowly towards equilibrium without oscillating
Critical damping – when the system returns to equilibrium as quickly as possible without overshooting (and oscillating)

Natural Frequency

Many objects (systems) can be set oscillating by applying some initial force. The system then oscillates naturally, without applying any further driving force. The frequency that the system oscillates naturally is called the natural frequency of the system.

Examples:

Attach a **ruler sticking out from the table**, and then twang it. It vibrates at a certain natural frequency. E.g. up and down 5 times per second would be 5 hertz or 5Hz (5 oscillations per second). The natural frequency of a ruler like this depends on the length sticking out.

Child on swing – pull back a child then release her – she will swing at a natural frequency (again, dependent on the length of the swing rope)

Mechanical Constructions such as bridges – must be designed to be slightly flexible, otherwise there is always a risk of breakage (and allowing slight flexing prevents this). If a bridge is jolted in some way it can oscillate (although damping usually minimises this) and good bridges are designed to be critically damped

Guitar strings, tuning forks, brass instruments, (all instruments in fact) are just a few other examples.

Essentially, everything that is able to oscillate also has its own natural frequency.

Forced Oscillations

A forced oscillation is simply an oscillation that is brought about and maintained by the application of a force

An example, again, is a child on a swing. If the child is pushed each time she swings, the oscillation is called a forced oscillation. The frequency at which the force is applied is called the frequency of the driving force, or the frequency of the forced oscillation.

Resonance

Resonance is a condition, or a description of an oscillating system. This condition is achieved when the frequency of the driving force is exactly equal to the natural frequency of the system being oscillated. When resonance is achieved, the amplitude of the system is maximised and will keep increasing unless it is dampened.

Example

Again, we shall refer to the child on a swing.

When the child is left to swing naturally suppose she does so with a frequency of 1 swing (out and back) every 2 seconds – so the period is equal to 2 seconds and the frequency; 0.5Hz

Suppose now a boy begins to push the child.

He starts by matching the natural frequency at which the child swings, i.e. 0.5Hz – so he applies the force once every 2 seconds (remember $f = \dfrac{1}{T} \Leftrightarrow T = \dfrac{1}{f}$)

He is able, without increasing the size of the force, to make the child swing higher and higher – amplitude keeps increasing. The boy's applied force (driving force) and the oscillating swing are said to be in resonance.

Now the boy decides to close his eyes and stand at an appropriate place where he can still push the girl. He applies a force, periodically and the same size as before. However this time, since he has his eyes closed, he does not quite match the natural frequency of the child swinging. The result will be that sometimes he will push too early, against the child and sometimes too late and will have reduced or no effect. The result will be that the amplitude of the oscillation will be reduced.

Useful examples of resonance

Violin – string is strummed with the bow so that resonance is achieved and sound is emitted

Microwave ovens – the frequency of the microwaves used match the natural frequency of water molecules and this causes amplitude of vibration to increase and heating to occur

Ultrasound to destroy (break up) kidney stones – ultrasound (high frequency sound) with a frequency that matches the natural frequency of the kidney stone crystals causing large amplitude vibration of particles and shattering of the stones

Examples where resonance is a nuisance

Aircraft shattering windows – frequencies of sounds emitted from certain jet engines can match the natural frequency of glass sheets (which would depend upon the size of the sheet). This causes large amplitude vibration and shattering if damping is insufficient

Bridge collapse – soldiers marching over a bridge always break step to avoid a continuous and significantly large oscillating driving force. If not, there is a chance that they could set up a vibration matching the natural frequency of the bridge and cause damage if this oscillation became too large. Famously, in 1940 a gusting wind set a Tacoma Bridge vibrating which resulted in its collapse. The designers had not considered correctly that it is not only the size of the force of a wind that needs to be taken into account, but also the resonance effect and the frequency of a gusting wind. Do a search on youtube to see this impressive bridge collapse.

Vibrations in cars – at certain speeds some cars (particularly older ones) or parts on the car, such as mirrors or the steering wheel, begin to vibrate. This is when the vibration caused by the engine (driving force) matches the natural frequency of the system. Such systems need damping mechanisms (e.g. rubber mounts) to counter this effect.

Wave Characteristics

Waves are the means by which energy is transferred. All waves also involve oscillations.

> **Note:**
> - energy, not matter, is transferred
> - there is actually no net (overall) transfer of energy resulting from a standing wave – energy is effectively reflected back and forth between two points
> - where there is a net transfer of energy, the wave is called a progressive wave.

To help understand the concepts of wave motion and particle motion within a wave, consider a side view of part of a water-wave with a cork floating on it, as follows:

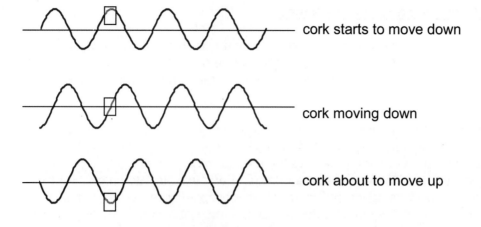

cork starts to move down

cork moving down

cork about to move up

- The wave shows 4 complete cycles, or oscillations
- Wavelength is, therefore, the total horizontal length of the wave shown divided by 4
- The wave is moving from left to right - this can be noted by the position of the crest that starts at the same position as the cork, and has moved forwards half a wavelength on the third wave shown
- The straight horizontal lines show the equilibrium position of the wave – this corresponds to the position of undisturbed water
- The energy movement corresponds to the wave movement: from left to right
- The motion of the particles (water molecules) is up and down – shown by the movement of the cork
- If the next 3 corresponding diagrams are drawn (as above) the wave would have moved forwards by one complete wavelength. The cork would have also moved through one complete oscillation (up and down). Hence, a wavelength corresponds to an oscillation of the vibrating particles.
- This (water wave) is an example of a transverse wave

Types of wave:

1) Longitudinal- "particle" oscillations (vibrations) are parallel to direction of wave.
2) Transverse   - "particle" oscillations are perpendicular to direction of wave motion

Note – particles are

- air atoms/molecules in case of sound waves (in air)
- water molecules in case of water waves
- electromagnetic field in case of electromagnetic radiation

More Terms to understand / learn

Wavelength

- the distance along the axis of the wave from one part of the wave to the next occurrence of this part (e.g. crest to crest or trough to trough)
- measured in metres
- symbol for wavelength is λ

Wave speed

- the speed that a wave travels. Can be found by finding the speed of a particular point on a wave – e.g. crest for a water wave. Can also be found by finding the rate at which energy is transferred – e.g. sound waves: measure how fast the sound travels

crest

- the point on a wave with maximum positive displacement

trough

- the point on a wave with maximum negative displacement

compression (maximum pressure)

- term used to describe region where particles (e.g. air molecules) are closer together than they would be in their normal equilibrium state.

Rarefaction (minimum pressure)

- term used to describe region where particles (e.g. air molecules) are further apart than they would be in their normal equilibrium state.

Intensity

- term used to describe the energy of a wave
- more intense light is brighter; more intense sound is louder
- *intensity* α *amplitude*^{2} so, if the amplitude of a wave doubles, the intensity (energy) of the wave multiplies by 4 (increases by a factor of 4)

Wave models (graphs)

The conventional sine-curve shaped wave is actually a mathematical graph showing the displacement of the particles within a wave, as follows. Pay particular attention to the description of the horizontal axes of each of the four graphs shown.

Transverse Waves

We should be familiar with two different graph representations:

displacement – at one instant in time

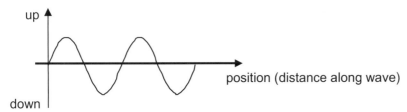

This wave shows how displacement varies along the wave. It is a good visual representation of a real transverse wave – for example, a water wave. Horizontal distance from peak to peak gives wavelength and the maximum height of the wave, from the wave axis (x axis on graph) gives us the amplitude of the wave – which corresponds to the maximum displacement of the particles in the wave. A picture of a water wave would give us this graph – with correct displacement; distance coordinates, measured directly off the picture.

displacement – at one position on the wave

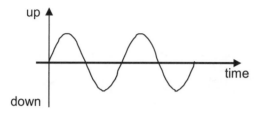

This wave shows how displacement at a single point on the wave varies as time progresses. It is therefore not a good visual representation of the wave – since if we can see the particles (e.g. water wave) we see the whole wave, not just a single point on the wave. This type of wave can easily be misinterpreted – horizontal "distance" from peak to peak on the graph does not give wavelength – because it is not a distance, it is a time. The time from peak to peak therefore gives the period of the wave and, as before, the maximum height of the wave, from the wave axis (x axis on graph) gives us the amplitude of the wave – which corresponds to the maximum displacement of the particles in the wave.

Longitudinal Waves

Again, we should be familiar with two different graph representations:

displacement – at one instant in time

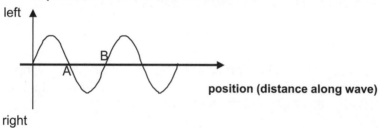

This wave shows how displacement varies along the wave. It is a not a good visual representation of a real longitudinal wave – for example, a sound wave – since the graph shows left displacement upwards, visually and right displacement down, visually. In reality we would see the particles moving to the left and right, parallel to the axis of the wave, and not up and down, perpendicular to the direction of wave propagation. Distance from peak to peak gives wavelength and the maximum height of the wave, from the wave axis (x axis on graph) gives us the amplitude of the wave – which corresponds to the maximum displacement (left or right) from the usual equilibrium position of the particles in the wave.

Longitudinal waves are often called compression waves because they consist of a series of compressions – where particles are closer together than usual, (compressed) – separated by rarefactions. In the wave-graph above, point A, where the graph first crosses the x-axis, corresponds to a rarefaction, since particles to the left are displaced leftwards (as shown by the upwards part of graph) and particles to the right are displaced to the right (as shown by the downwards part of graph). Using a similar explanation, point B corresponds to a compression, as does the origin point of the graph.

displacement – at one position on the wave

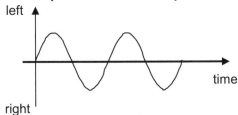

This wave shows how displacement at one point on the wave varies as time progresses. Using similar arguments to those used in the previous two graphs, it is a not a good visual representation of a real longitudinal wave. Distance from peak to peak gives period and the maximum height of the wave, from the wave axis (x axis on graph) gives us the amplitude of the wave – which corresponds to the maximum displacement (left or right) of the particles in the wave.

Wave Relationships

One wavelength on a displacement / time graph represents the period of the wave
One wavelength on a displacement / position graph represents the wavelength of the wave

For all waves: wave speed   =   frequency   x   wavelength

$$\{ v = f \ x \ \lambda \}$$

Derivation:

- distance travelled by wave per second = number of waves passing a point per second x length of each wave
- but speed of wave = distance travelled by wave per second
- speed of wave = number of waves passing a point per second x length of each wave (wavelength)
- but number of waves passing a point per second = frequency

.∴ *speed of wave = frequency x wavelength*

Example T4.4

(a) calculate the frequency of gamma rays with a wavelength of $3.8 \times 10^{-13} m$

(b) calculate the speed of sound in air given that the wavelength of a middle C note has a frequency of 256Hz and a wavelength of 1.30m

(c) a canoeist riding waves is at one moment at the peak of a wave and 0.4 seconds later is at the next trough of the wave. Given that the wave peaks are 2.5 metres apart, calculate the speed of these waves.

Electromagnetic Spectrum (EMS)

The EMS is a group of waves that are all forms of electromagnetic radiation: rather than oscillating matter, they consist of oscillating electric and magnetic fields.

All waves in the EMS travel at the same speed (speed of light, c) ie. $3.0 \times 10^8 \, ms^{-1}$ (in a vacuum)

You need to know the waves in the electromagnetic spectrum, and their approximate wavelengths. This information is as follows:

Use the mnemonic: GAXUVIMR to remember the waves in order of wavelength, shortest first

$10^{-15} m$	Ga	- gamma rays
$10^{-12} m$	X	X rays
$10^{-9} m$	Uv	Ultra-Violet radiation
$10^{-7} m$	V	Visible radiation (light)
$10^{-5} m$	Ir	Infra-red radiation
$10^{-2} m$	M	Microwaves
$10m$	R	Radio waves

It should be noted that each type of wave in the list above actually has a range of wavelengths. The different wavelengths, for example, of visible light give us the different colours of the visible spectrum (ROYGBIV)

Example T4.5

Using the fact that audible sound has a frequency range of 20 Hz to 20 kHz and travels at 330ms⁻¹ and using the data given above, do some calculations and to describe how sound wave frequencies compare to those of waves in the EMS

The Behaviour of Waves

Reflection
- when a wave meets a surface it may be reflected
- angle of incidence = angle of reflection
- wave can be reflected, transmitted or absorbed by a medium
- the wave may refract as well as reflect on entering the new medium

Refraction
- wave enters a new medium
- speed changes
- wavelength changes
- frequency remains the same
- direction changes (unless incident angle = 0°)

If wave enters a medium in which it travels slower:

- its speed decreases
- its wavelength decreases
- its frequency remains the same
- it bends towards the normal

Example – light passing through air, then a glass prism

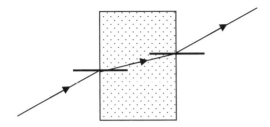

Notes:

- The light bends towards the normal (line perpendicular to surface-boundary) as it enters the "slower" medium (glass)
- Waves never bend past the normal line
- The amount of bending (ie. the angles) can be calculated using Snell's Law (covered later)
- The light bends away from the normal as it passes from the glass to the "faster" medium (air)
- The ray entering the glass prism is parallel to the ray emerging from the prism because the two faces of the prism are parallel and the amount of bending at the first surface is the same as the amount of "unbending" at the second.

Snell's law

Snell's law connects the speed, wavelength and direction of an incident wave with that of the same wave once it has been refracted.

Snell's Law states that, for a certain boundary (e.g. air → glass) the following ratios are always the same, whatever the incident angle:

speed in medium 1 : speed in medium 2

wavelength in medium 1 : wavelength in medium 2

sine of angle in medium 1 : sine of angle in medium 2

The following diagram explains this in more detail.

For a ray refracted as follows:

speed c_1
wavelength λ_1
angle from normal θ_1

speed c_2
wavelength λ_2
angle from normal θ_2

$$\frac{c_1}{c_2} = \frac{\lambda_1}{\lambda_2} = \frac{\sin \theta_1}{\sin \theta_2} = a\ constant\ \text{(refractive index)}$$

If medium 1 is a vacuum or air, the constant is called the refractive index of the second substance. The refractive index therefore tells us how much faster light is in air than in the second medium (e.g. glass).

Example T4.6

Light is shone into a glass block (prism) at an angle of 47° to the normal (i.e. angle of incidence = 47°). It emerges at 29° to the normal.
(Note: light can be taken to travel at the same speed in air as in a vacuum – and the speed in a vacuum is given in the data booklet)

- (a) find the refractive index of the glass used in the prism
- (b) find the speed of light in this glass
- (c) if the wavelength of light in the glass is 600nm, calculate the wavelength of the light in the air
- (d) calculate the frequency of this light in air
- (e) calculate the frequency of this light in the glass

Example T4.7

Light travels at 3.00×10^8 ms^{-1} in air and 2.07×10^8 ms^{-1} in glass. If a light ray is shone into a glass prism at 30° to the surface of the prism (as shown), find the angle of the light ray inside the prism, and draw and label this ray on the diagram

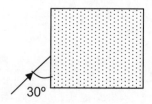

Refraction and Reflection at a medium

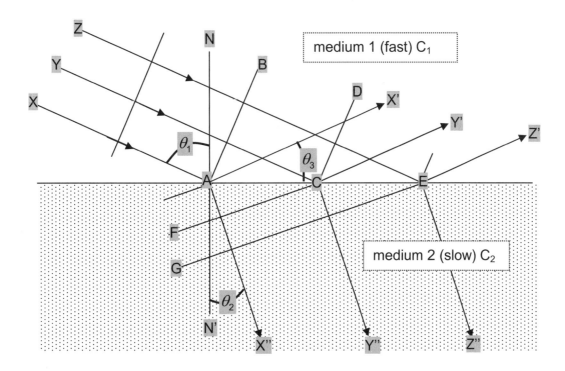

The above diagram shows a wave travelling in medium 1 and approaching a new medium, medium 2. The wave travels slower in medium 2 than in medium 1. As the wave enters medium 2 it refracts, slowing down and bending towards the normal. It also reflects, bouncing back into medium 1 at an equal speed and the angle of the reflection is equal to the angle of incidence.

This wave could be any kind of wave: water, sound or light, for example.
The new medium for water would be, for example, a shallower section of water (where it travels slower). For light the boundary may be air, then glass or perhaps air then water, for example. For sound, the boundary could be air then water (say, in a swimming pool) or warm air, then cold air)

A wave can be considered as a beam. Three rays are shown on this beam: X, Y and Z.

Wavefronts are lines that move forward with the wave, perpendicular to the wave direction (ray). The incident wave has wavefronts AB and CD, for example.

The wavelength is the distance between consecutive wavefronts

The wave reflects, emerging at X', Y' and Z' and the angle of incidence, θ_1, is equal to the angle of reflection, $90° - \theta_3$

The wave also refracts when the rays meet at A, C and E, emerging at X", Y" and Z". the angle of refraction is θ_2

Given the speed of the wave in medium 1 is C_1 and the speed in medium 2 is C_2, we can use Snell's law as follows:

$$\frac{c_1}{c_2} = \frac{\sin\theta_1}{\sin\theta_2} = \frac{\lambda_1}{\lambda_2} \, a \text{ constant } \textit{for this boundary}$$

Diffraction

When a wave meets the edge of a solid object it may be deviated from its path. Diffraction is most noticeable when a wave passes through a gap in a solid object and the effect is more pronounced when the gap is about the same size as the wavelength of the waves (can be greater or smaller than wavelength, there is no precision here).

Examples of Diffraction

i) Sound waves passing through a doorway, or past the corner of a building, can be heard "around the corner" (as well as in the expected regions!)

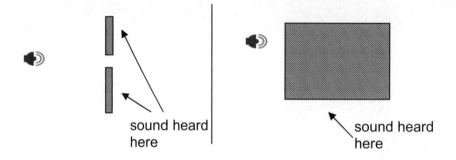

ii) water waves – ripples show wavefronts and wave-direction

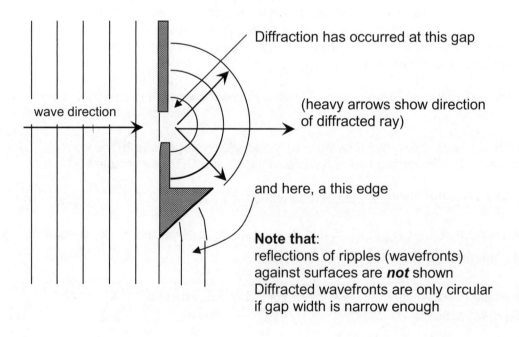

Diffraction has occurred at this gap

(heavy arrows show direction of diffracted ray)

and here, a this edge

Note that:
reflections of ripples (wavefronts) against surfaces are **not** shown
Diffracted wavefronts are only circular if gap width is narrow enough

iii) Light passing through a narrow slit

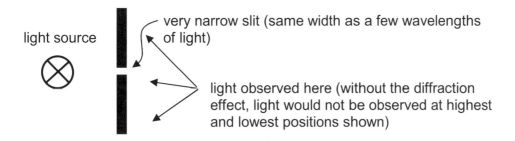

light source

very narrow slit (same width as a few wavelengths of light)

light observed here (without the diffraction effect, light would not be observed at highest and lowest positions shown)

Interference

When two or more waves exist at the same time, they may interfere with each other, producing a "resultant" wave. Examples: Sound – two speakers in phase with one another (i.e. producing compressions and rarefactions at the same time) – in different regions in the space surrounding the speakers, sound of low and high volume (loudness) can be observed. Water waves: when two crests from two different waves meet, they combine to form a higher crest (supercrest). Light – light from two different points (but have to be from same initial source) directed on to a screen – bright and dark areas can be observed on the screen.

In each example mentioned above, the change in intensity (loudness for sound, brightness for light etc.) depends on how the waves at the point (place) in question meet each other. The Principle of Superposition can be used to explain these intensity changes:

Principle of Superposition

When two or more waves (have to be the same type of wave) meet, the total displacement at any point is the sum of the displacements that each individual wave would cause at that point

To illustrate this, imagine sound is being observed at a single point. Over time, repeated rarefactions and compressions will be observed (the sound wave). Consider the waves from each source individually:

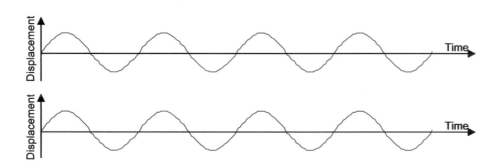

At all points in time the two waves are in phase (i.e. crests occur at the same time, as do troughs). This results in constructive interference, as follows:

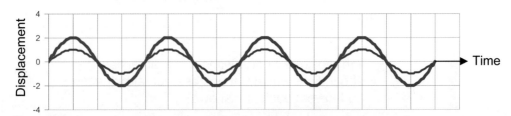

(displacement axis not to same scale as above waves)

The red coloured curve shows the displacement of both the individual waves (they are on top of each other, so they appear as one)
The thick blue curve is obtained by applying the principle of superposition – the displacement at each point along the wave is obtained by adding together the displacements of each red wave
The amplitude (maximum displacement) of the resultant wave is thus double that of either red wave so this is constructive interference.

Now consider two waves that are out of phase (a crest from one source is observed at the same time as a trough from the other):

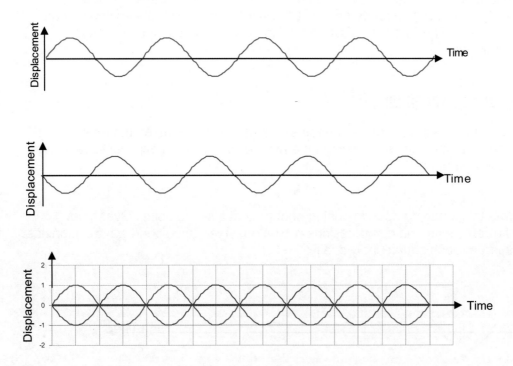

The blue wave is found by adding the individual displacements of the red and green waves – and since they are always of opposite sign (and equal magnitude) they cancel – the result is a "null" wave – no sound would be observed

Finally let us consider two waves that are not in phase but not completely out of phase:

Example T4.8

Draw in the blue line, using the principle of superposition

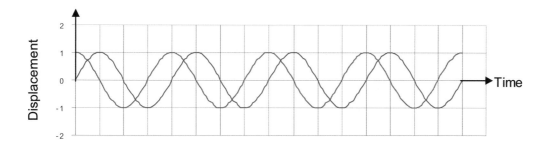

The blue wave is the result of the simultaneous existence of the red and the green wave. Consider time 0: green wave displacement+ red wave displacement = 1 + 0 = 1 Therefore resultant displacement at time, 0 is 1
At time corresponding to 1 unit on the graph: green displacement = 0, red = 1 therefore total =1, and, after 2 units of time total displacement = −1 (green) + 0 (red) = −1, etc.

Note that maximum resultant displacement is greater than either individual displacement, so we have constructive interference

This effect (and principle) applies to all types of wave, for example light, water, and sound.

Topic 5 – Electric Circuits

Electric Potential Difference, Current and Resistance

Overview

In order to make an electric appliance work, an electric circuit is needed. Essentially, electric devices work when electrons contained in the wires of the device are caused to move. This movement generally results in the production of a magnetic field and a heating effect. Both of these results are very useful: the heating effect can produce useful heat, light and other forms of radiation, and the magnetic field can be used to produce force and movement – and can therefore be used in a huge variety of electric motor devices, ranging from hair driers to stereo systems, to electric/hybrid cars.

So the electric circuit basically consists of the wiring in the actual device, attached to connecting external wires, attached to a battery or other electrical supply, attached back to the device. The whole affair thus forms a loop. Essentially, the power supply provides a force field. The force field is not magnetic but electric: it exerts force on charged particles – like electrons. The external connecting wires thus transmit the force field to the wiring in the electrical device and the result is that electrons within the device (wiring) move. As stated earlier, this then causes a heating effect and/or a magnetic effect, and the device does work (converts energy).

This topic addresses how and why electrons in circuits move and ways to measure "electricity" and the energy changes that occur.

Electric Current

An electric current is said to flow when charged particles move. For this part of the course we consider only circuit electricity where the electric current flows in metallic wires. Since, in metals, the only particles that can move around are free electrons these are the charges responsible for current flow.

Electric current is defined to be the rate of flow of charge (electrons)
Electric current is measured in amps (A).
Charge is measured in coulombs (C)

Therefore, 1A = 1C per second $1A = 1Cs^{-1}$

Equation: $I = \dfrac{q}{t}$ where $I = current, \quad q = charge, \quad t = time$

As given in the data booklet, a single electron has a charge of $1.6 \times 10^{-19} C$ (actually we should, strictly, include a minus sign since an electron is negatively charged). We can therefore deduce that to give a current of 1A, we need 6.25×10^{18} flowing past a point (in the wire) per second.

The unit of current, the ampere (or amp), is defined as the current needed when flowing through two parallel wires placed 1 metre apart in a vacuum, in order to produce a certain magnetic force between the wires.

Electric Potential Difference

Electric potential difference is also referred to simply as voltage.

Electric potential difference is measured in volts.

To understand electric potential difference at a simplistic level, consider one coulomb of electrons moving around a circuit. They come out of the power supply freshly fuelled with energy (electric potential energy). It is a 6 volt (6V) power supply, so the coulomb of electrons has exactly 6 joules (6J) of energy available. As they move through the thick connecting wires they do so effectively without losing any energy. The electric potential energy drop is therefore zero, so far. Next they move through the appliance. Assuming that this is the only appliance in the circuit, they will lose all their energy as they pass through the appliance. The potential energy difference of the electrons, from the point where they enter the appliance to the point where they leave, will therefore be 6J. The voltage across the appliance will therefore be 6V. When the electrons return to the power supply, they will be 6J lower in energy than when they started. The potential difference across the appliance is therefore 6V.

From the above passage it would appear that potential difference is energy difference. The subtle difference is that potential difference is potential energy difference per unit charge (coulomb).

Before considering the following definition, remember that energy difference = energy converted = work done.

Electric Potential Difference - Definition

The electric potential difference between two points is the work done per unit charge in moving a charge from one point to the other:

$$\Delta V = \frac{work\ done}{charge} = \frac{W}{q}$$ (equation NOT GIVEN in Data booklet)

This is the same as saying that potential difference is the potential energy difference per unit charge, when the charge moves from one point to another.

Potential difference is measured in volts.

Explanatory example:

Suppose a power supply is connected up. The + side will attract electrons and the − side will repel them. Electrons will therefore experience a force. This force causes the electrons to move and so we have work being done (work done = force x distance). (Recall that if we have work done, we have a conversion of energy – this energy may be heat or movement, for example)

Suppose that the work done by each electron is $3.8 \times 10^{-17} J$ (energies are very small with electrons)

We know that the charge of one electron is $1.6 \times 10^{-19} C$

$$\Delta V = \frac{W}{q} = \frac{3.8 \times 10^{-17}}{1.6 \times 10^{-19}} = 237.5 \approx 240V$$

So, if a circuit is connected up and the result is that each electron releases $3.8 \times 10^{-17} J$ when passing from one point to another, then the potential difference between these two points must be 240 volts.

Note that the power supply is used to provide this potential difference, via the electric field that it produces – so a 240V power supply would be needed in the above example.

Example T5.1

The potential energy difference between an electron at point A and electron at point B is 1.08 x 10^{-17} J. Find the potential difference between the points.

Electric Potential

Voltage is the quantity that measures the potential energy *difference* (per unit charge) across two points in a circuit. It is also the quantity that measures the actual potential energy per coulomb of a charge. This quantity is called, simply, potential. For example the negative plate of a 2V cell ("battery") may have a potential of −1V and the positive plate; +1V. The potential difference across the cell is, therefore 2V (1V − − 1V = 1V + 1V = 2V) and the cell can deliver 2J per coulomb of electrons that pass through the cell.

The Electronvolt

A useful unit of energy in atomic and nuclear physics (with such small energies often involved) is the electronvolt.

One electronvolt is the energy associated with an electron moving through a potential difference of one volt.

This energy is the same as the work done on or by the electron when the field is applied.

Thus, using $\Delta V = \frac{W}{q} \Rightarrow W = q\Delta V = 1.6 \times 10^{-19} C \times 1V = 1.6 \times 10^{-19} J$

So, $1 \ electronvolt = 1.6 \times 10^{-19} \ joules$ or: $1eV = 1.6 \times 10^{-19} J$

In simple terms, to convert joules to electronvolts divide by 1.6×10^{-19}

To convert electronvolts to joules, multiply by 1.6×10^{-19}

Example T5.2

Find the energy released when an electron moves through a potential difference of magnitude 500V

Note that the symbol, e, is often used for the charge of an electron, 1.6×10^{-19} C.

Electrical Resistance

Electrical resistance is a property of a material that measures its ability to allow current to flow. High resistance materials thus hinder current flow and low resistance materials allow easy passage of current. A block of wood, being an electrical insulator, effectively has infinite resistance, whilst a lump of iron, being a conductor, has effectively zero resistance. Other materials have resistance somewhere in between.

Electrical resistance is measured in ohms
The symbol for ohms is Ω

Resistance – Definition

The resistance of a material (or device) is the ratio of the voltage across the material to the current flowing through the material.

Defining equation: $R = \dfrac{V}{I}$

where $R = resistance,\ V = voltage,\ I = current$

So, to measure the resistance of an electrical device or material we can connect it up to a power supply (using any safe voltage) and measure this voltage and the current through the device. Resistance is simply voltage divided by current.

Current, Resistance and Resistivity

The rate at which charge flows depends on the velocity of the charges. The velocity of the charges is called drift velocity

(For ohmic conductors – see below) the speed (drift velocity) of electrons in a conductor depends on:

1) cross-sectional area of conductor
2) length of conductor
3) material from which conductor is made
4) temperature of conductor

resistance of conductor

5) potential difference (voltage) across conductor

The resistivity of a material is a measure of the resistance of a certain material. We can find the resistivity of various materials in data-books or on the internet and we can then find the electrical resistance of, for example, a wire made of this material using the following formula:

$$R = \frac{\rho L}{A}$$ where
$R = resistance \ (\Omega)$ $\rho \ ("rho") = resistivity \ (\Omega m)$
$L = length \ (m)$ $A = cross \ sectional \ area \ (m^2)$

As we can see above, resistivity is measured in ohm-metres (Ωm)

Example T5.3

Given that copper has a resistivity of $1.72 \times 10^{-8} \Omega m$ at 20°C, calculate the resistance of a piece of copper wire with a diameter of 1.00mm and a length of 5cm at 20°C.

Note that, generally, as the temperature of a metallic material increases its resistivity (and therefore resistance) increases. This can be explained in terms of the atoms in the metal vibrating at an increasing rate at higher temperatures and hindering the progress of passing electrons.

Ohm's Law:

"The current through a wire is proportional to the potential difference across it, provided the temperature is unchanged"

Ohm's law equation:

$$R = \frac{V}{I}$$

Ohm's law effectively states that the resistance, R, is constant - and does not change if current (or voltage) is increased as long as the material is not allowed to heat up.

Generally, metallic conductors obey Ohm's Law.

Ohmic and non-ohmic behaviour

A conductor is said to be ohmic if the current flowing through the conductor is proportional to the potential difference across the conductor (i.e. one for which resistance remains constant).

An easy and effective way to observe this behaviour is to plot current versus potential difference for a range of voltages.

Examples

Wire (metallic conductor)

Filament Lamp

Semiconductor Diode

The only graph for which $V \alpha I$ is the first. The wire is thus ohmic and the other two are non-ohmic. Note that if a very large current is forced through the wire, it will become non-ohmic (like the lamp).

A lamp is non- ohmic because the filament gets very hot as current is increased. This causes resistance to increase. The gradient of the IV graph hence decreases.

A diode is non-ohmic because if the potential difference is reversed, no current flows: resistance is infinite. For the wire and lamp the direction of the current (and potential difference) makes no difference to the way they behave, as conductors. Semiconductor diodes generally have an effective resistance of zero at 0.3V

Electrical Power:

Power is defined as the rate of doing work

$$Power = \frac{work\ done}{time\ taken}$$, assuming work is done at a constant rate

But $work\ done, W = q\Delta V$, as stated earlier

Hence, Power = $\dfrac{qV}{t}$

but, for a constant current, $q = I\,t \Rightarrow$ Power = $\dfrac{I\,t\,V}{t} \Rightarrow$ Power = $I\,V$

So, electrical power delivered by a resistor (conductor) is equal to the product of the potential difference across the resistor and the current flowing through the resistor.

$$P = VI$$

Other expressions for power – derivations:

$$P = VI, \ but \ V = IR,$$
$$\Rightarrow P = (IR)I = I^2R$$
$$P = VI, but \ I = \frac{V}{R}$$
$$\Rightarrow P = V\left(\frac{V}{R}\right) = \frac{V^2}{R}$$

Summary

$$P = VI$$
$$P = I^2R$$
$$P = \frac{V^2}{R}$$

Note that any of these equations can be used in any situations. Sometimes one yields a quicker answer than another.

Example T5.4

A circuit has a single resistor, with a resistance of 30Ω, connected to a 12V power supply

   a) Find the current flowing through the resistor
   b) Find the power delivered through the resistor

EMF   (ElectroMotive Force)

Refers to a source of electrical energy.

The emf of a source is equal to the electrical energy produced per unit charge inside the source. Unit: Volt.

In simple terms, the emf of a source is the maximum possible voltage of the source. Some of this voltage is "lost" because the source itself has a resistance – so the apparent voltage of the power supply, and the voltage across the external resistor, will be a little lower than the emf of the power supply (source)

So – not all energy is converted to electrical energy outside the source since some is lost inside the source due to internal resistance.

Internal resistance - the resistance of a source

Example T5.5

An 8.0V power supply is connected to a 12Ω resistor. The voltage across the resistor is measured as 7.68V and the current; 0.64A. Explain the voltage drop, and explain (with any necessary calculations) what the emf is and the what internal resistance of the supply is.

Resistance in Series and Parallel Circuits

Series circuits

Consider the following circuit, which has a cell with an emf of V_T volts, negligible internal resistance and is connected in series to 3 resistances, of R_1, R_2 and R_3 ohms respectively. A current, I, flows around the circuit, as shown:

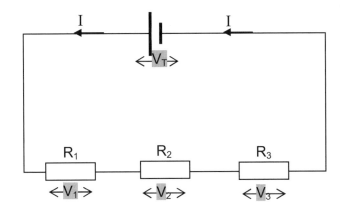

The same current, I, flows through all resistors

Let the total resistance of the circuit be R_T

The total voltage is therefore: $V_T = IR_T$

But also, the total potential difference (pd) across resistors in series is equal to the sum of the pds across the individual resistors, i.e.:

$$V_T = V_1 + V_2 + V_3$$

But, $V_1 = IR_1, V_2 = IR_2, V_3 = IR_3$

Hence,
$$V_T = IR_1 + IR_2 + IR_3 = I(R_1 + R_2 + R_3)$$
$$V_T = I(R_1 + R_2 + R_3)$$

But, $V_T = IR_T$

Hence
$$\boxed{R_T = R_1 + R_2 + R_3}$$

Parallel circuits

Consider the following circuit, which has a cell with an emf of V_T volts, negligible internal resistance and is connected to 3 resistances in parallel to one another, of resistance R_1, R_2 and R_3 ohms respectively. A current, I, flows around the circuit, as shown:

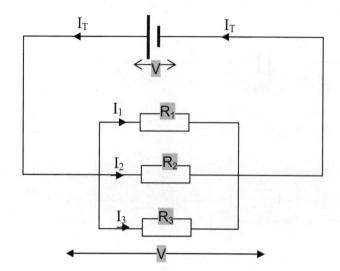

The potential difference across any branch of a parallel circuit is equal.

Therefore, V(across R_1)= V(across R_2)=V(across R_3)=V(of cell)

Let the total resistance of the circuit be R_T. The total voltage is: $V = I_T R_T$

But also, the total current around the circuit (and through the cell) is equal to the sum of the currents through each branch of the parallel part of the circuit. I.e.,

$$I_T = I_1 + I_2 + I_3$$

But, $V = I_1 R_1, V = I_2 R_2, V = I_3 R_3$

$$\Rightarrow I_1 = \frac{V}{R_1}, I_2 = \frac{V}{R_2}, I_3 = \frac{V}{R_3}$$

$$I_T = I_1 + I_2 + I_3 \Rightarrow I_T = \frac{V}{R_1} + \frac{V}{R_2} + \frac{V}{R_3}$$

But also: $V = I_T R_T \Rightarrow I_T = \frac{V}{R_T}$

Hence: $\dfrac{V}{R_T} = \dfrac{V}{R_1} + \dfrac{V}{R_2} + \dfrac{V}{R_3} \Rightarrow$ $\boxed{\dfrac{1}{R_T} = \dfrac{1}{R_1} + \dfrac{1}{R_2} + \dfrac{1}{R_3}}$

Example T5.6

Consider the following circuit, and complete the table below:

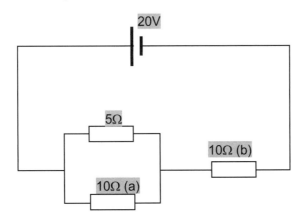

	5Ω	10Ω (a)	10Ω (b)	Total circuit
Voltage				
Current				
Resistance				
Power				
Charge passed in 1 sec				

Some tips to start you off!

- start by finding the total circuit resistance
- then find total circuit current (from total resistance and voltage)
- next find pd across 10Ω resistance in series
- find current through each of the two resistors in parallel, using V=IR
- find power dissipated by each resistor using P=VI (or one of other formulae), charge passed using Q=It

(**note**: there are usually many different ways of solving circuit problems – they all (obviously) lead to the same solutions!)

Voltmeters and Ammeters

Correct positioning

- Ammeters are placed in series with the part of the circuit they are to measure – so that all the current has to pass through the ammeter
- Voltmeters are placed in parallel (across) the part of the circuit they are measuring – so that virtually no current has to pass through the voltmeter.

i.e.:

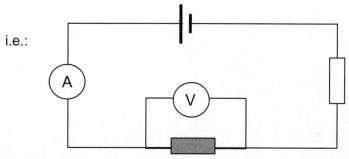

An ideal voltmeter has infinite (in practice, very large) resistance
An ideal ammeter has zero (in practice, very small) resistance

Deviations from ideality lead to the meters changing the circuit they are measuring.

For example, the above circuit is used to measure the potential difference across the grey resistor shown and the ammeter, to measure the current through the resistor.

If the ammeter was not ideal it would have significant resistance and reduce the current it is attempting to measure. Further, it would alter the potential difference across the resistor, since it would also take a share of the supply voltage.

If the voltmeter was not ideal it would have a relatively low resistance and would reduce the resistance between the points either side of the resistor. This would also reduce the potential difference that it is attempting to measure. Further, it would alter the current measurement made by the ammeter, since it would also allow current to flow (through it), increasing the current reading made by the ammeter.

Example T5.7

A battery has an internal resistance of 10Ω and is connected to an external resistance of 100Ω. A voltmeter is connected across the external resistor, as shown below. It gives a reading of 10V:

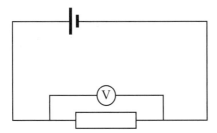

(a) Find the current flowing in the circuit
(b) Find the potential difference across the internal resistance
(c) Hence, state the emf of the battery
(d) What assumption about the voltmeter have you made in your calculations?
(e) If a different voltmeter was placed in the circuit, and this new voltmeter had a resistance of 60Ω, what reading would the voltmeter now give?

Notes:

The internal resistance of a source is approximately constant, BUT the voltage "lost" across the internal resistance depends on the current flowing in the circuit and through the supply, which depends on the size of the total external resistance.

The smaller the external resistance, the greater the pd across the internal resistance. (for example, in the above example – (a) to (c), the emf of the supply is 11V, but only 10V is available to the external resistor. If however, the internal resistance is equal to the external resistance, only half the emf value would be available for the external resistor)

Potential Dividers

A potential divider is a circuit that is able to vary (divide) the potential difference of the supply.

This is particularly useful for students doing experiments involving varying the voltage (potential difference) when they do not have a variable voltage power supply.

A common potential divider circuit involves a rheostat (wound wire resistor – as in the picture. The resistance is varied by changing the length of the wire that the current passes through via the sliding terminal in the middle.

The circuit below shows potential divider being used to vary the voltage across a bulb.

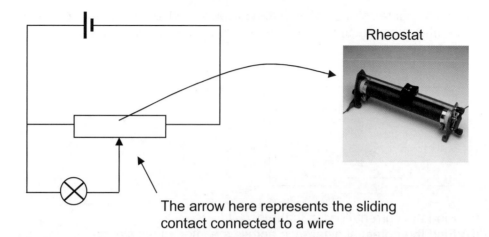

Rheostat

The arrow here represents the sliding contact connected to a wire

Potential Dividers as sense/response circuits

Potential Divider Circuits can also involve the use of two resistors in series, rather than using a rheostat. This set-up is useful for electronic sensor circuits – since one of the resistors is a sensor, and its resistance controls the split of the total potential difference across both resistors.

Example: LDR potential divider circuit

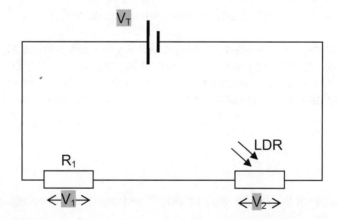

An LDR is a light dependent resistor: its resistance changes as the level of light changes.

If light increases, the resistance of the LDR decreases, V_2 decreases and V_1 increases

The fixed resistor, R_1, can be attached to a meter or can form part of an alarm system, or any other device. The essential point here is that the voltage across the fixed resistor, R_1 is controlled by the LDR.

The sensor resistor could also be a temperature dependent resistor (thermistor) or strain gauge (resistance depends on physical strain-force)

Topic 6 – Fields and Forces

This topic seeks to compare and understand the basics of three types of field: Gravitational fields, Electric fields and Magnetic fields.

The theory for all three types of field is quite similar, especially for the former two types.

In this chapter, I shall refer to **"object"** to mean either mass, charge or moving charge. Explanations follow.

Some introductory basics about charge

There are two types of electric charge: positive and negative. The smallest unit of charge is the charge of an electron: $-1.6 \times 10^{-19} C$. A proton has a charge of equal magnitude, but positive. The charge of any charged object (e.g. ion, metal sphere, plate etc.) will therefore be an exact multiple of $1.6 \times 10^{-19} C$. Charge can be neutralised by the presence of the opposite charge. Electrically neutral objects therefore must have equal numbers of protons and electrons. An object can be charged either by adding or removing electrons (protons, being part of the nucleus, are difficult to remove) or by moving electrons from one region to another. So an imbalance in distribution of negative and positive charge also results in an object becoming charged.

Conservation of charge

Charge is always conserved. It cannot be destroyed. For example, if electrons are removed from one object, they must go to another object.
This law (conservation of charge) also explains why current cannot diminish in a circuit: so in a simple series circuit the current is the same at all points in the circuit. If a resistor is added to the circuit this will reduce the current in all parts of the circuit.

Conductors and Insulators

As discussed in Topic 5, electrical conductors allow the passage of charge (electrons) and electrical insulators do not. This is because conductors contain free electrons: electrons that are able to move within the network of atoms. Electrons in insulators are all attached firmly to the atoms: there are no free electrons in insulators.

Charging by friction

A simple way to charge an object is to simply rub it – this is called charging by friction. The object becomes charged since when you rub it you transfer electrons either to or from the object, giving it an imbalance of charge.

However, if you rub a conductor the imbalance of charge is immediately balanced by the free electrons nearby (there may still be a tiny overall imbalance but this is spread over the entire object and therefore not noticeable).

If you rub an insulator (like a comb) with a cloth, it will become charged. The area that was rubbed will have an excess of protons or an excess of electrons and there are no free electrons to counter this imbalance. You can then use the comb to pick up tiny pieces of paper or bend flowing water (neutral objects are attracted since they still contain electrons or protons that can be attracted).

Comparison of Fields

What is a field?

A **field** is a region in space (a place) where an "object" experiences a **force** due to its presence in the field. The interaction between the object and the field causes the force on the object.

A **gravitational field** is a place where a **mass** experiences a force
An **electric field** is a place where an **electric charge** (e.g. electron, proton or ion) experiences a force
A **magnetic field** is a place where a magnet experiences a force

Note that a magnet is produced, essentially, by the movement of charge (electrons) so the last statement can be replaced by:

A **magnetic field** is a place where a **moving charge** (e.g. electron, proton or ion) experiences a force

What produces a field?

A **gravitational field** is produced by a **mass**
An **electric field** is produced by a **charge** (example proton, electron or ion)
A **magnetic field** is produced by a **moving charge** (example moving proton, electron or ion)

Field lines

Gravitational field lines are the lines followed by **masses**

Electric field lines are the lines followed by *positive* **charges** (so negative charges would move along the lines in the opposite direction)

Magnetic field lines (more complicated) are the lines that plotting compasses or magnets align themselves to (different from the other two – they are not the lines followed by moving charges)

Field patterns (shapes):

Gravitational Field for a point mass (same for a planet)

Approximate Gravitational field for a planet surface

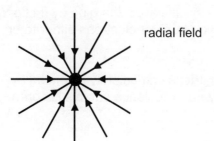

radial field

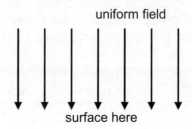

uniform field

surface here

Electric Field Lines (Shapes)

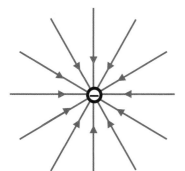

Negative point charge
(radial field)

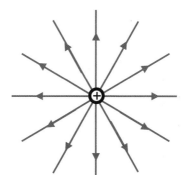

Positive point charge
(radial field)

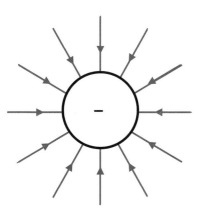

Negative sphere
(radial field)

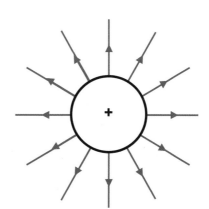

Positive sphere
(radial field)

Opposite point charges

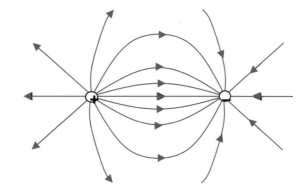

Like point charges

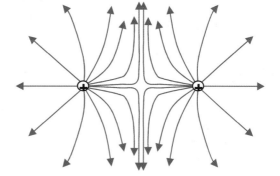

Parallel plates – oppositely charged.

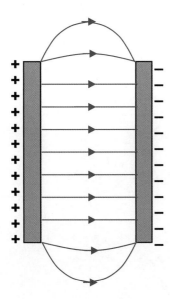

It is easy to predict the shape of the field (direction of field lines) in all of the above cases – just think about the direction that a positive charge (e.g. proton) would follow.

We can see the similarities between electric and gravitational field lines – point (or spherical charges) and masses have the same shape (although field lines for positive point charges go in the opposite direction.

Magnetic Field Lines (shapes)

There will be a magnetic field around any *moving* charge

Bar magnet

("magnetic lines of force (field lines) always flow away from north")

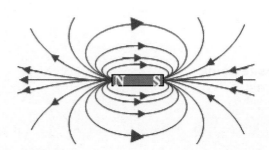

Straight current-carrying conductor

Use "screw rule" to predict the direction of the field lines

Note the X represents current going into the page

To make a screw go into page, turn screwdriver clockwise – like field lines

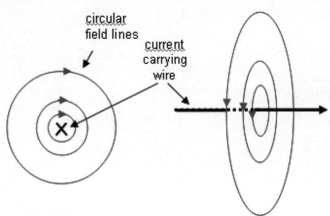

circular field lines

current carrying wire

Flat Current-carrying Coil

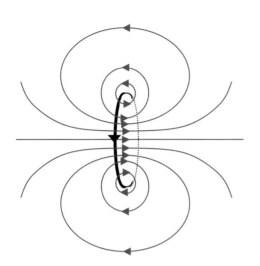

Notes

- The black circle represents the current-carrying wire and the blue curves; the field lines
- Only a cross-section of the field line pattern is shown. The field lines also go in and out of the plane of the paper, with the same pattern as shown in the diagram.
- The power-source for the current carrying wire is not shown
- The field lines follow the same arrangement (but there are more, and closer together) if several coils of wire are used.

A current carrying solenoid (tubular coil of wire)

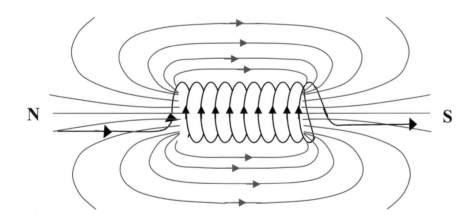

Note the similarity between (i) this diagram and the diagram for a flat, single coil (as previous) (ii) this diagram and the diagram showing the field pattern for a bar magnet. To determine direction of field lines (coloured blue) imagine looking down either end of the solenoid. Note whether current is flowing clockwise or anti-clockwise.

If clockwise ⇒ S (the letter S has ends pointing in clockwise direction) ⇒ South pole (and lines of force point AWAY from north – i.e. towards south)

If anti-clockwise ⇒ N (the letter N has ends pointing in anti-clockwise direction) ⇒ North pole (and lines of force point AWAY from north). Thus, on the above diagram there will be a north pole on the left hand end and a south pole on the right.

Strength of field from field lines

For all fields the strength of the field is indicated on the field line diagram by the spacing of the field lines: the greater the spacing the weaker the field.

Field strength

Field strength is a quantity that describes the strength of the force exerted by a field on an object placed in the field.

Definitions:

The field strength of a **gravitational field** is the **force per unit mass** (kilogram) experienced by a small mass placed in the field.

The field strength of an **electric field** is the **force per unit charge** (coulomb) experienced by a positive test charge placed in the field.

(a test charge is a charge small enough not to affect the field that it is in)

The field strength of a **magnetic field** is the **force per unit current length** on a current carrying wire placed in the field.

Units of field strength and Equations

Gravitational field strength:

symbol	g,
units:	newtons per kilogram (Nkg^{-1})
Equation:	$g = \dfrac{F}{m}$

Electric field strength:

symbol	E
units:	newtons per coulomb (NC^{-1})
Equation:	$E = \dfrac{F}{q}$

Magnetic field strength:

symbol	B
units:	Tesla (equivalent to newtons per amp-metre)
Equation:	$B = \dfrac{F}{IL}$

Example T6.1

Find the field strength of the following fields, and name the type of field in each case:
   (a) One which exerts a force of 98N on a 10kg mass
   (b) One which exerts a force of 4.8×10^{-17} N on a stationary electron
   (c) One which exerts a force of 24mN on a 30cm length of wire carrying a current of 1.25A

Forces between objects in fields

Masses

Every mass has its own gravitational field. This field does not affect the mass itself, but another mass placed in its vicinity will be affected. The second mass will also have its own gravitational field which will affect the first. These two forces experienced by the masses will, regardless of the size of each mass, be equal in magnitude and opposite in direction (the masses attract each other). This is in accordance with Newton's third law. The size of the force on each mass is given by the equation:

$$F = G\frac{m_1 m_2}{r^2}$$ where:

G is the universal constant of gravitation

m_1, m_2 are the values for the two masses

r is the distance between centres of the masses

This equation is known as Newton's universal law of gravitation. It can be applied to any two masses in the universe: all masses attract each other. The value of G is given in the data booklet.

Charges

Using the same argument as the one for masses, there will be a force between charges in proximity to each other.

Like masses, the force on each charge will be the same magnitude. However, with charges, the forces can be attractive or repulsive, depending the type of each charge (+ or −). Forces will, of course, be opposite in direction. The size of the force on each charge is given by the equation:

$$F = k\frac{q_1 q_2}{r^2}$$ where:

k is the coulomb constant

q_1, q_2 are the values for the two charges

r is the distance between centres of the charges

This equation is known as Coulomb's law. It can be applied to any two charges. Note that charges exert electric forces on each other whether they are stationary or moving. (But if they are moving they will also exert magnetic forces on each other). The value of k is given in the data booklet.

So the theory and mathematical treatment for the force between charges is almost identical to that for the force between masses (the only difference is that, for charges, the force can be attractive or repulsive but for masses the force is always attractive).

Example T6.2

Find the forces involved and draw force diagrams for the following interactions:

    (a) Two masses, 500kg and 1000kg, 5cm apart
    (b) A proton and a helium 2+ ion, 1.2×10^{-12} m apart

Forces on and between moving charges are more complicated and not similar to those for electric and gravitational fields – they will be discussed later.

Fields due to objects

We can now derive equations for the field due to a mass or charge. Again, the mathematical treatment and equations are very similar.

Gravitational field due to mass

We are going to derive the expression for the field due to (and surrounding) mass M.

If mass m is placed in the vicinity of mass M, the force on mass m due to the field caused by mass M is $F = G\dfrac{m_1 m_2}{r^2}$ (m_1 = m, m_2 = M)

By definition, the field strength of the field caused by M is given by the force per unit mass when a mass is placed in the field.

In this situation, mass m is placed in the field, and it experiences a force $F = G\dfrac{m_1 m_2}{r^2}$.

Hence the field strength caused by M is given by the expression:

$$g = \frac{F}{m} = \frac{\left(G\dfrac{Mm}{r^2}\right)}{m} = G\frac{M}{r^2}$$

So, the field strength, g, (caused by a mass M), distance r from the centre of this mass (M), is given by the equation:

$$g = G\frac{M}{r^2}$$

Electric field due to charge

Using the same treatment, the field strength, E, caused by charge q, distance r from the centre of this charge, is given by the equation:

$$E = k\frac{q}{r^2}$$

Example T6.3

Find the field strength in the following cases:
(a) 1.0mm from an electron
(b) 10cm from a 50kg mass

This example makes the point that forces between masses around us are too small to be significant. To have noticeable forces one needs either very large masses or very small distances (and the latter situation requires very high density materials).

Combining fields

It is important to note that fields are vector quantities: they have magnitude and direction. Therefore, to combine the effect of two or more fields, one must sum each contribution using vector addition.

Example T6.4

(a) find the field strength midway between an electron and a proton placed 5mm apart
(b) state the field strength midway between two planets of equal mass
(c) find the field strength at point P, in the vicinity of an electron and a proton at the vertex of a right angled triangle as shown below:

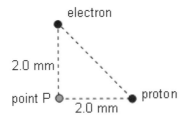

Magnetic Forces

Force on a conductor in a magnetic field:

When a current carrying conductor (i.e. wire) is placed in a magnetic field, the conductor has its own magnetic field, so the two will interact. Depending on the orientation of the wire relative to the field there will therefore be a force on the wire and it will move, if allowed. There are three things to consider: the direction of the field in which the current is placed, the direction of the current in the wire and the direction of force (or motion). Two of these variables must be known in order to calculate the third. Fleming's **left** hand rule may be used, as follows:

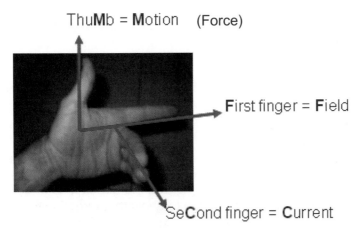

Note:
- The blue lines are all orthogonal (at 90°) to each other
- Current is **conventional** current
- There are other rules you may have come across for making these predictions - it doesn't matter which one you use

Example T6.5

A wire is placed next to the north
end of a bar magnet, as follows:

Describe the direction of the force
experienced by the wire

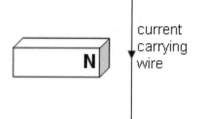

Force on a charge moving through a magnetic field

A moving charge can also be considered to be a current, for this is how a current is
defined. However, it is important to remember that conventional current is opposite to
the direction that electrons move.

Therefore, in order to predict the direction of the force on a charge moving in a
magnetic field, first consider whether it is a positive charge (direction = same direction
as current) or a negative charge (direction = opposite direction to current) and then
simply use Fleming's left hand rule, as before. Note though, that the thumb gives the
force on the charge (the motion will result from this force and from the motion it
already has)

Example T6.6

The following diagram shows two charges, an electron and a proton moving through a
magnetic field, shown by the blue crosses. The proton is coloured red and the
electron, black. The arrows drawn in already show the direction of motion of the two
particles. Label each charge with an arrow, labeled F, showing the direction of force
acting on it.

Note:

Crosses are used for field lines or current to indicate that the direction is directly away
– i.e. into the page. Dots are used (less commonly) to show that direction to be out of
the page. Sometimes larger crosses are used, or even a large single cross.

Magnetic Field Strength

Magnetic field strength has the symbol, B and the unit, Tesla (T).
I have already mentioned the way that field lines can be used to indicate relative field strength. It is also possible to calculate the magnitude (size) of the force.

Definition:

Magnetic field strength is defined to be the force per unit length per unit current on a current carrying conductor at right angles (90°) to the field lines.

Equation:

$$B = \frac{F}{IL} \text{ where,}$$

$B = magnetic\ field\ strength$

$F = force\ on\ wire\ at\ right\ angles\ to\ field$

$I = current\ in\ wire$

$L = length\ of\ wire\ exposed\ to\ field$

This equation can obviously be used to find the 4th variable if the other 3 are known.

Example T6.7

A wire carrying 0.8A is placed at 90°
to a field (shown in blue on diagram),
of strength 0.25T. The length of wire
exposed to the field is 40cm. Find the
magnitude and direction of the force
acting on the wire.

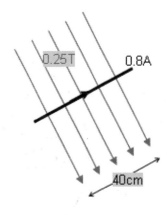

Topic 7 – Atomic and Nuclear Physics

Atomic Structure

Nuclear Model

The currently accepted model of the atom is that it is spherical and composed of a central, very small and dense nucleus that is surrounded by "shells" of electrons, orbiting the nucleus.

The nucleus contains protons (positively charged) and neutrons (no charge – neutral), of approximately equal mass. The electrons are negative and are therefore attracted to the positively charged nucleus. This attraction, together with the momentum of the electrons, causes the electrons to orbit the nucleus in the same way that planets orbit stars. Electrons are virtually massless, and are considered to occupy no volume.

Evidence for this model was first provided by Geiger and Marsden, in the early 20th century.

Rutherford's/Geiger & Marsden's Alpha scattering Experiment

Experimental:

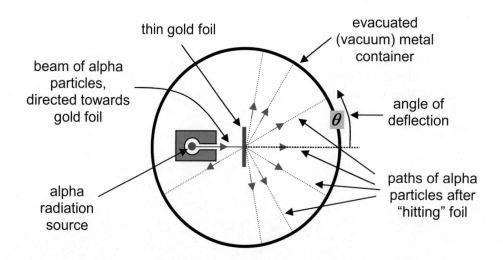

Note: *Alpha particles are helium nuclei (He^{2+}), which are very small, positively charged particles.*

Results:

1. most particles passed straight through the foil, with no significant deflection
2. about 1 in 1800 particles was deflected by angles between 0° and 90°
3. about 1 in 8000 particles "bounced" backwards, at an angle greater than 90°

Explanation of results

1. given that the foil was around 400 layers of gold atoms thick, from result 1 above, it was concluded that the atom must be composed mostly of space (calculations show that an atom is about 10,000 times larger than its nucleus: atomic diameter $\approx 10^{-10}\,\boldsymbol{m}$, nuclear diameter $\approx 10^{-14}\,\boldsymbol{m}$)
2. these deflections were attributed to the fact that the gold nuclei are positive, and so are the alpha particles – so, when an alpha particle passes close to a gold nucleus (not very often, due to 1, above) it is repelled, and deflected. The amount by which it is deflected depends on how close it passes by the gold nucleus.
3. These deflections were explained by the fact that in a very few cases, the alpha particle actually collides with a gold nucleus, and therefore bounces back.

These observations and explanations can be summarized using the following diagram (which is worth drawing in most exam questions referring to this experiment)

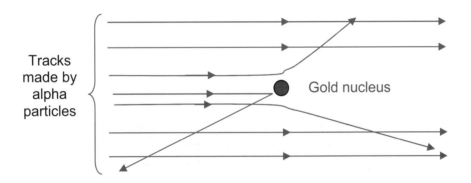

Follow up calculations:

Size of atom: $\approx 10^{-10}\,\boldsymbol{m}$
Size of nucleus $\approx 10^{-14}\,\boldsymbol{m}$

Limitation of the model of the atom as a small nucleus surrounded by orbiting electrons

The model does not account for how the protons and neutrons stay together in the nucleus: at such short ranges the protons should repel each other enormously and fly apart.

Atomic Energy Levels

It is now accepted that electrons occupy "shells" surrounding the nucleus. Each shell corresponds to a certain energy level that the electrons occupying the shell have. An energy level of zero corresponds to the electron escaping from the atom. Electrons "attached" to an atom have energy levels with negative values. The further away the electron from the nucleus, the higher the energy level. Thus, to promote an electron from one shell to a shell further from the nucleus, i.e. to move it from one energy level to a higher energy level, energy must be put in. Conversely, if an electron relaxes back, dropping to a lower energy level, energy is released.

Atomic emission and absorption spectra provide us with experimental evidence for these atomic energy levels.

Emission Spectra:

When certain substances are excited by some external source of energy, e.g. heat, light or electricity, they can become illuminated. For example, Neon tubes glow when stimulated by electricity. Sodium lamps appear yellow. An emission spectrum is a spectrum showing wavelengths (and frequencies) of light emitted. The light emitted is usually split up (dispersed) using a prism or diffraction grating.

When tungsten is heated strongly it emits a white light. White light consists of a continuous spectrum of all the colours in the visible spectrum (red, orange, yellow, etc). So if the light from a tungsten filament is dispersed using a prism and viewed on a screen, the following is observed:

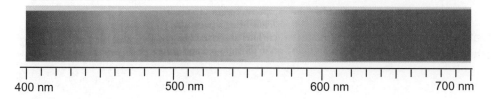

The scale shows the how the wavelength of light varies with colour.

Sodium vapour in a gas discharge tube (vapour is excited by high voltage) results in the following emission spectrum:

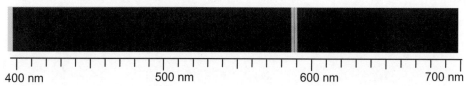

If white light is shone through sodium vapour, the following absorption spectrum results:

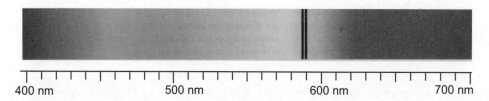

The last two spectra above are called line spectra, because lines of light are emitted or absorbed. It is no coincidence that the lines for the two spectra above correspond to the same wavelengths – it is because they originate from the same energy level jump in the same atom. The wavelength is the wavelength of light emitted or absorbed when electrons jump from one particular energy level to another. If they jump to a higher level, they absorb the light; if they jump to a lower level they emit light (there are many other, less distinct and bright lines for sodium corresponding to jumps to and from different energy levels)

Different elements have different energy levels corresponding to particular "shells" and require different amounts of energy to jump from one level to the next. Therefore line spectra provide a very accurate way of identifying the presence of a minute amount of a particular element in a sample.

Photons

Experimentation shows that light behaves not only as a wave-like energy, but also as a particle beam. A particle of light is called a photon. In an emission line spectrum, for example, like the one shown above, only light photons with the exact same energy as the energy involved in the electron jump will be emitted. The energy of a photon depends on the frequency of light, and the colour of light depends on the frequency, so a line with a certain colour will be emitted.

Energy of a photon

The energy of a photon depends on the frequency (and, therefore wavelength). The higher the frequency (lower the wavelength) the greater the photon-energy.

$$E = photon\ energy\ (J)$$

Equation: $E = hf$ where $h = Planck's\ constant\ (6.63 \times 10^{-34} Js)$

$$f = frequency\ of\ light\ (Hz)$$

Nuclear Structure

As stated earlier, an atom is made up of a central nucleus and surrounding electrons. The nucleus is composed of protons and neutrons.

- The number of protons is called the atomic number (sometimes also called proton number)
- Nucleons is the collective term for protons and/or neutrons. So the number of nucleons in an atom is the total number (sum) of protons and neutrons.
- The number of nucleons (protons + neutrons) is called the mass number (also sometimes called the nucleon number)
- A nuclide refers to an atom with a particular nucleus configuration – referring simply to an atom is ambiguous because it could be one of two or more possible isotopes. It is common to refer to nuclides using their chemical symbol followed by their mass number. For example the nuclide with 53 protons and 74 neutrons is I-127 (Iodine 127).

General Symbol of the nuclide:

$$X = the\ element$$

$_{Z}^{A}X$ where $A = nucleon\ number\ (protons + neutrons)$

$$Z = protons$$

So neutron number N is equal to $A - Z$

Elements are defined by their atomic number. For any particular element, the atomic number does not change (for example, it is possible for an atom of the element oxygen to have 8 electrons or 10 electrons and it is possible for an atom of oxygen to have 8 neutrons, 9 neutrons or 10 neutrons, but, to be an oxygen atom, it must have 8 protons. An oxygen atom is defined to be an atom of the element with atomic number 8.

Some atoms of the same element have different masses. This mass difference is attributed to the fact that they contain different numbers of neutrons.

Atoms with the same atomic number (i.e. atoms of the same element) but different mass numbers are called isotopes. Two different isotopes of the same element therefore are different because they contain different numbers of neutrons.

Example T7.1

Uranium is an element with chemical symbol U, and it has an atomic number of 92. Two common isotopes of uranium have 145 and 146 neutrons in their nuclei.

> (a) Name the two nuclides in this example
> (b) For the nuclide with the greatest atomic mass, state its atomic mass, and nucleon number and how many protons and neutrons it has

Nuclear Forces

It may seem surprising that a nucleus stays together, given that it is composed only of positive and neutral particles. To understand why this is so, it is necessary to outline the forces that exist in a nucleus. Three types of force exist in a nucleus:

Gravitational force – an attractive force between particles with masses. Very weak compared to the other two

Electrical force – the repulsive force that the protons exert on each other. This force is immense compared to the gravitational force of attraction and would, without the existence of another attractive force, cause the nucleus to fly apart

Strong force – simply called "strong force" or "strong nuclear force" this force is about 100 times as strong as the electrical force in the nucleus. Unlike the electrical and gravitational forces, it has a very short range, reaching only as far as from one nucleon to its neighbour.

Radioactive Decay

Chemical reactions involve the electrons within an atom. The nuclei of the atoms taking part in chemical reactions never change.
Nuclear reactions, however, involve one or more nucleus changing.

Some nuclei are more stable than others. When an unstable nucleus disintegrates (breaks apart) to acquire a more stable state, radiations are emitted. This phenomenon is called radioactivity or radioactive decay. This reaction is spontaneous and most commonly involves the emission of an alpha particle (α particle) or beta particle (β particle).

In both α emission and β emission the parent nucleus undergoes a change of atomic number and therefore becomes the nucleus of a different element. This new nucleus is called the daughter nucleus or the decay product. It often happens that the daughter nucleus is in an excited state when it is formed, in which case it reaches its ground state by emitting a third type of radiation called a gamma ray (γ ray)

Beta decay: the antineutrino

When a nuclide undergoes beta decay two particles are observed products of the reaction: the daughter nucleus and the β^- particle.

In such reactions, the β^- particles emitted have a range of energies, up to a certain maximum energy.

Based on these observations alone, this should not be possible: if the daughter nuclide has a certain energy, the β^- particle should then take the remainder of the energy and all beta particles, therefore, should have the same energy, corresponding to the maximum β^- particle energy actually observed.

The observations, then, leave us to question where the missing energy has gone. This question was answered very recently. There is in fact a third particle emitted in β^- decay reactions: the antineutrino ($\bar{\nu}$).

Example: The β^- decay of chlorine-36:

First suggestion: $$^{36}_{17}Cl \longrightarrow {}^{36}_{18}Ar + {}^{0}_{-1}\beta$$

This reaction is balanced in terms of mass and proton number. However, as discussed, the β^- particles have a range of energies up to a certain maximum value, rather than all having the expected maximum value.

The correct reaction is thus: $$^{36}_{17}Cl \longrightarrow {}^{36}_{18}Ar + {}^{0}_{-1}\beta + \bar{\nu}$$

Properties of the Radiations

Property	α-particle	β-particle	γ-ray
Symbol	$_{2}^{4}\alpha$	$_{-1}^{0}\beta$	γ or $_{0}^{0}\gamma$
Production	loss of 2p+2n from Parent	Parent n → p+e (e emitted)	daughter nucleus relaxes → energy
Nature	Helium nucleus	Fast electron	EMR
Charge	+2e	-e	0
Rest Mass	4.0015u	.00055u	0
Velocity	≈ .06c	Up to 0.98c	c
Energy	≈ 6MeV	≈1 MeV	≈ 0.1MeV
Ionization power	≈ 10^5	10^3	10
Path through matter	straight	tortuous – (not at all straight!)	Straight
Deflection by a magnetic field	deflected	deflected strongly	not deflected
Penetration	≈ 5cm air	≈ 500cm air ≈ 0.1cm aluminium	≈ 4cm of lead reduces intensity to 10%

Note c = speed of light   EMR = Electro-Magnetic-Radiation

Ionizing properties of radiation

These radiations are able to ionize matter as they pass through it. They do this by knocking electrons off of atoms in the matter through which they pass. α-particles are so strongly ionizing because they are not only charged, but they also are quite massive – certainly compared to electrons (β-particles) and γ-rays.

The ability for these radiations to ionize matter makes it possible to detect them. The ionization chamber (cloud chamber) contains a gas that when ionized shows causes condensation of a vapour also contained in the chamber – so when radiation passes through it the tracks can be seen, rather like miniature clouds as left behind an aeroplane flying through the air.

The Geiger-Muller tube (GM tube) also relies on the ionization of a gas in an electric field, connected to a high voltage circuit. The ions so created move, effectively completing the circuit and allow current to flow in the circuit. The current created works an electronic counter, connected to the circuit. A GM tube is therefore a good means of measuring the level of radiation emitted from a radioactive sample.

Biological Effects of Ionising Radiation

When an ionising radiation is exposed to animal tissue, electrons can be knocked off tissue cells. This can cause atoms to be broken off of molecules. The structure of cells can thus be changed. This can then result in abnormal functioning of the cell (for example zero reproduction, or uncontrolled reproduction of the cell – cancer) or cell death.

Examples of radiation damage include: skin burns, ulceration, sterility, cataracts, cancer, decreased life expectancy.

Stability of Nuclei

The stability of a nucleus depends on the number of protons compared to neutrons. Iron-56 is one of the most stable nuclei. Nuclei lighter than iron-56 therefore tend to increase their stability by increasing in mass (i.e. undergoing nuclear fusion reactions) and those heavier than iron-56 tend to split apart, undergoing fission. Note that in both cases net energy is released, but a large amount of energy is often required to initiate the reaction – particularly in fusion reactions.

Radioactive nuclei disintegrate spontaneously; the process cannot be speeded up or slowed down. It follows that for large numbers of any particular species of nuclei the rate of decay is proportional to the number of parent nuclei present. (the parent nucleus is the original nucleus, before the nuclear reaction and the (one or more) nucleus produced is called the daughter nucleus or decay product(s)).

It is impossible to predict when any particular nucleus will disintegrate, but it is possible to say what proportion of a large number of nuclei will disintegrate at any given time.

For any particular nuclide, radioactive life = infinity

Half-Life

The half life of a radioactive substance is the time taken for the number (or mass) of radioactive nuclei present to fall to half its value. This length of time is constant at any point in time – showing that radioactive decay is exponential.

Example T7.2

The half-life of a certain radioactive material is 6 minutes. What fraction of a sample of the material will decay in half an hour?

Example T7.3

The following decay shows how the mass of a particular radioactive sample varies with time. Use the graph to find the half-life of the sample.

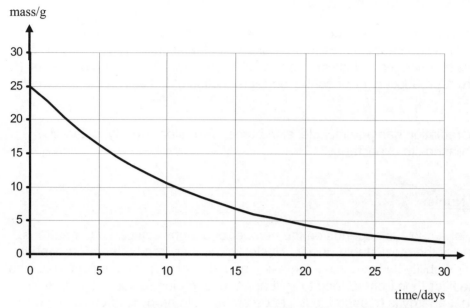

Note that to find the half-life from a decay curve, the time taken for the mass or activity of the sample to half is found – ANY starting point can be used. For example, try finding the time taken for the mass of the above sample to decrease from 10g to 5g – you should get the same answer, 8 days (approximately).

Radioactive decay curves such as the one above show exponential decay – the quantity reduces to half its value in constant time.

Nuclear Reactions

Artificial Transmutation

This is the name given to the process whereby a nucleus is artificially made from another nucleus (or nuclei). It is different from regular radioactivity, or radioactive decay, in that the reaction is not spontaneous; it is made to happen (hence artificial). It was discovered in 1918 (by Rutherford) in the following experiment:

When nitrogen gas was bombarded by α-particles it was found that there were two products: oxygen gas and positively charged particles, which were lighter than α-particles.

It was proposed and later proved that the second product consisted of protons.

Thus: $_7^{14}N \; + \; _2^4He \; \rightarrow \; _8^{17}O \; + \; _1^1P$

This experiment was famous since it was responsible for the discovery of the proton as part of the nucleus (and for the discovery of artificial transmutation!)

Balancing Nuclear Reaction Equations

Balancing chemical reactions involves balancing the number of each type of atom (element) on the left and right hand side of the equation.
However, with nuclear reactions elements can change but the total mass (i.e. all mass numbers added up) and total atomic number are the same on both sides of the equation.

Example T7.4

In the following decay reaction, find the values of **a,b,c,d,e,f**:

$$_b^a Po \rightarrow \ _d^c\alpha + \ _{82}^{206}Pb + \ _f^e\gamma$$

Example T7.5

Complete the following nuclear reactions by adding in any mass or proton numbers and any other products.

a) $\ _{92}^{238}U \ \rightarrow \ Th \ + \ \alpha$

b) $\ _6^{14}C \ \rightarrow \ _7^{14}N \ +$

c) $\ _{27}^{60}Co \ \rightarrow \ Ni^* \ + \ \beta$
$$\downarrow$$
$$Ni \ + \ \gamma$$

Unified Mass Unit

In chemistry, masses of nucleons are expressed in atomic mass units. In physics, we need to be more precise (for example, we shall see that protons and neutrons have slightly different masses) and to use S.I. units for mass. Nucleons are therefore measured in terms of the unified mass unit, u, as follows:

$$1u = 1.661 \times 10^{-27} \, kg$$

mass of an electron, $m_e = 0.000549u$
mass of a proton, $m_p = 1.007276u$ all given in data book
mass of a neutron, $m_n = 1.008665u$

Mass – Energy Equivalence

If an object increases in energy – for example, gets hotter, or moves more quickly, then its mass also increases. The effect is not noticeable on an "every-day" scale but, on a nuclear scale this effect becomes significant.
The relationship between mass and energy is described by Einstein's famous equation:

$E = mc^2$ where : E = energy, in joules

m = mass, in kilograms

c = speed of light = $3.00 \times 10^8 \, ms^{-1}$

When energy is released, for example by a nuclear reactor, there is also a decrease in mass of the products, compared with reactants.

Example T7.6

Calculate the amount of energy accompanying a 1.00 gram fuel mass-loss in a reactor.

Mass Defect and Binding Energy

Since energy is required to break up a nucleus into its constituent parts (protons and neutrons), energy must be added. This energy is called binding energy since it is the energy associated with the binding together of the nucleons – and numerically equal to the energy required to separate them. Using the above idea of mass energy equivalence, mass is also therefore added when energy is added.

It follows that the mass of a nucleus is less than the total mass of all the separate protons and neutrons making it up. This difference in mass is called the mass defect of the nucleus.

Mass defect (for a nucleus) = total mass of separate nucleons – mass of nucleus

Mass defect (for an atom) = total mass of separate nucleons + electrons – mass of nucleus

Example T7.7

A helium atom has a mass of 4.00260u. Find the mass defect and the binding energy of a helium atom.

Fission and Fusion

A useful measure of the stability of a nucleus is its binding energy per nucleon. This is the energy that needs to be supplied to remove a nucleon from the nucleus. Nuclides that have the largest binding energy per nucleon are therefore the most stable.

The following graph shows how binding energy per nucleon varies with the mass number (nucleon number)

Binding Energy per nucleon graph

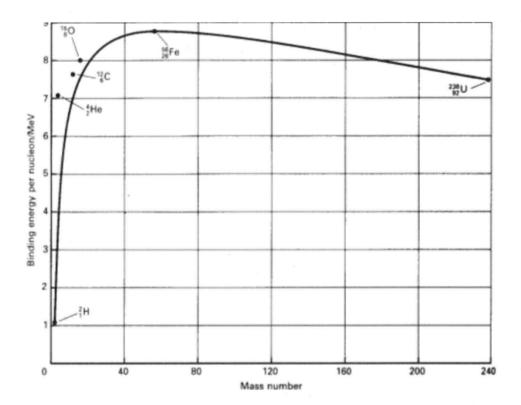

Nucleons in iron have the most binding energy, so are the most stable. Therefore iron (iron-56) is the most stable nuclide. As can be seen from the graph, the further either side of iron you go, the less stable the nuclide. Nuclides therefore become more stable if they change in mass closer to that of the mass of iron. Therefore nuclides heavier than iron tend to break apart (undergo fission reactions) and nuclides lighter than iron tend to join (fuse) with other light nuclides, undergoing fusion reactions.

When nuclides undergo fission or fusion reactions to produce more stable nuclides, energy is always released. This can be a little confusing, so to explain, remember:

Binding energy = energy you have to put in to break nucleus apart

Hence: High binding energy nuclide → low binding energy nuclide
(put energy in)

and   Low binding energy nuclide → high binding energy nuclide
(energy is released)

This is the theory that allows us to release energy in nuclear reactions, e.g. in nuclear power stations.

Example T7.8

Using the graph above, predict which is the most stable nuclide:
Pb-206 or Po-210, and whether energy will be released or
absorbed in the following reaction. Find the quantity of this
energy release/absorption

$$^{210}_{84}Po \rightarrow \, ^{206}_{82}Pb + \, ^{4}_{2}He$$

Mass of $^{210}_{84}Po = 209.983u$

Mass of $^{206}_{82}Pb = 205.974u$

Mass of $^{4}_{2}He = 4.003u$

Further Notes

In order to make a nuclear fusion reaction take place, the reacting nuclei must approach
each other at incredibly high speeds (to overcome electrostatic repulsion). One way of
attaining these speeds is to use very high temperatures (about 100 million °C) –
thermonuclear fusion reactions. So far, no one has managed to produce a controlled
thermonuclear fusion reaction – bombs have been made using thermonuclear reactions –
but these involve chain reactions, which are not controlled.

The sun's energy comes from fusion reactions, and many heavier nuclei are produced
from fusion of hydrogen nuclei.

Topic 8: Energy, Power and Climate Change

Energy Degradation and Power Generation

Laws of Thermodynamics

1. "The complete conversion of energy from a heat source into mechanical work is not possible"

This means that a heat engines can never be 100% efficient – even if we could reduce all friction to zero. So, for example, if the heat engine burns fuel to create 100J of heat energy, we can never get 100J of useful mechanical work out. The maximum amount of energy we get out actually depends on the temperature that the engine runs at, and the temperature of the surroundings.

2. "To maximise conversion of thermal energy to mechanical work, a cyclical process must be used"

This means that we must convert heat energy to mechanical energy in continually repeating stages and not in one single stage. We can see this in all practical applications. Mechanical devices that burn fuel, to create heat, to make an engine run, always work in cycles. For example petrol and diesel engines often work at several thousand cycles per second. (The cycles in a 4-stroke car engine are as follows: (i) air/fuel is drawn in (ii) air/fuel is compressed (iii) fuel is ignited and power is created (heat converted to work) (iv) exhaust gases are expelled. This cycle is then repeated several thousand times per second.)

Energy Degradation

Energy degradation is the process whereby energy is transferred out of a useful system. The most degraded energy is heat energy and is difficult to utilise.

Power Production

A variety of power stations are now employed, with the increasing use of renewable fuel power stations such as hydroelectric power stations.

However, fossil fuelled power stations such as coal, gas and oil are still the world's main producers.

A typical coal fired power station

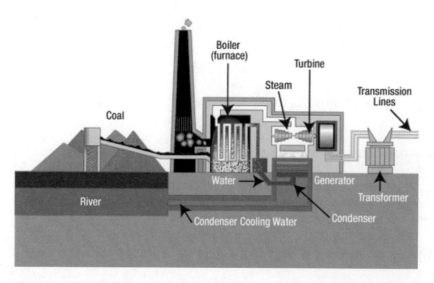

Boiler (furnace)

Turbine

Steam

Transmission Lines

Coal

Water

Generator

Transformer

River

Condenser Cooling Water

Condenser

Simplified description of processes

Coal, containing chemical energy, is burned and the thermal energy released is used to heat up water to produce pressurized steam. This pressurized steam is used to drive turbines. Turbines are very large cylindrical drums constructed so as to rotate using the force of the steam. The turbines are connected to huge coils of wire, in generators. The coils of wire move through a magnetic field (generators are constructed with very large electromagnets to create this field) and this causes an electric current to be induced (produced) in the wires of the coils. Therefore electricity has been produced. Of the total energy available originally in the fuel (coal, oil etc.) somewhere between around 30% and 50% is actually converted into electrical energy. The remainder is dissipated (wasted) as heat. This loss of heat is largely unavoidable and in accordance with the laws of thermodynamics. However, the efficiency of a power station can be significantly improved by actually using this dissipated heat for other purposes. This is increasingly being done, with rising fuel prices and increasing political pressure to increase energy efficiency. For example, in the Middle East, power stations often use this excess heat for desalination of salt-water. Power stations that re-use this heat by-product are termed CHP (Combined Heat and Power) plants.

Energy Diagrams

We represent the energy processes happening in a power station such as this using either energy chain diagrams or Sankey diagrams.

Energy Chain Diagram

This shows the basic energy transfers taking place, from the input energy (in the fuel) to the output: the electricity.

The following is an annotated energy chain for a coal fired power station.

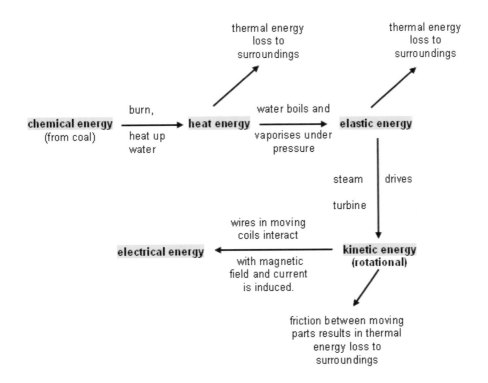

Sankey Diagram

A Sankey diagram is an arrow representation of the flow of energy and its transfers and energy dissipations in the process from input to output. The relative thickness of each part of the arrow (shown with little arrows) corresponds to the amount (proportion) of energy involved in each stage. In a very visual way, the diagram gives an idea of the overall efficiency of the process by comparing the thickness of the useful energy output with that of the input (energy from fuel).

By making approximate measurements you will find that the efficiency of the process represented by the Sankey diagram below (showing, again the coal fired power station process) is approximately 40%.

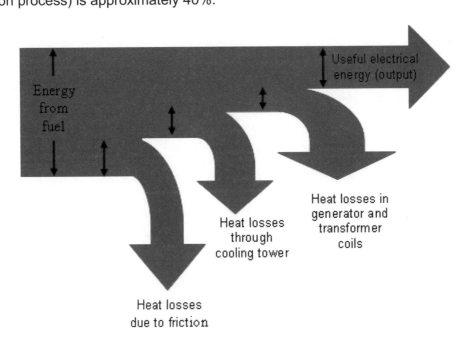

Note that the diagram is not very useful for making any precise measurements.

Note also that the Sankey diagram would be very similar for any thermal (heat producing) power station.

World Energy Sources

An energy resource is something that can provide us with usable energy.

A renewable energy resource is one that is replenished naturally and within a short time scale.

A non-renewable resource is one that cannot be replaced (in the foreseeable future) once used.

Renewable:

Hydroelectric Power
Geothermal Power
Tidal Power
Solar Power
Wind Power
Wave Power
Biomass

Non Renewable:

Oil and gas
Coal
Nuclear Power (but virtually unlimited)

CO_2 emission and environmental issues

Since all fossil fuels (and, essentially all organic substances) burn to produce CO_2, the three non-renewable fuels above all involve a contribution of carbon to our atmosphere (and contribute to possible global warming). In addition, Biomass is a CO_2 producer, since this form of energy production also involves burning organic matter. However, if biomass is not burned it decomposes into methane gas. Methane gas is a much more harmful gas to our environment that CO_2, so overall using Biomass is beneficial.

Energy Density

The energy density of a fuel measures the energy release from the fuel per kilogram of the fuel. It is a useful way of comparing fuel economy, particularly where transport of the fuel is involved.

Equation: $$energy\ density = \frac{energy\ released\ from\ fuel}{mass\ of\ fuel\ used}$$

In the exam, you will be expected to be able to compare fuels with different energy densities – the values will always be given.

World's Energy Resources Utilisation Breakdown (in 2004)

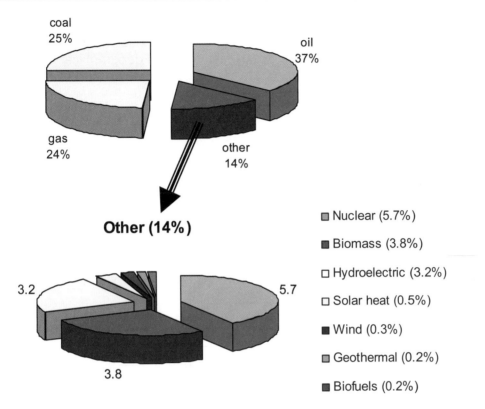

coal
25%

oil
37%

gas
24%

other
14%

Other (14%)

3.2

5.7

3.8

- ▨ Nuclear (5.7%)
- ■ Biomass (3.8%)
- ☐ Hydroelectric (3.2%)
- ☐ Solar heat (0.5%)
- ■ Wind (0.3%)
- ▨ Geothermal (0.2%)
- ■ Biofuels (0.2%)

You are expected to learn these approximate proportions and to discuss relative advantages and disadvantages of each, as an energy resource.

Key arguments will be fuel cost, set up cost (power station) environmental factors (e.g. CO_2 emission, pollution including sight, noise), sustainability, safety (nuclear presents problems), social acceptability and political pressures.

Ultimate Source of Energy

The vast majority of energy available on the Earth has come, directly or indirectly, from the sun.

Production of carbohydrates and thus all organic animal and vegetable material, including fossil fuels, came from the sun via photosynthesis and the food chain.

In addition to storages of energy on the earth in all the resources discussed, the sun continues to provide energy as it shines on to the Earth.

Approximately $8.5 \times 10^{16} J$ of the sun's energy reaches the Earth every second. The total world energy consumption in 2005 was approximately $5 \times 10^{20} J$. Using these figures, if we were able to collect all the sun's energy it would take less than 2 hours to give us enough energy for a whole year!!!

So energy shortage is not the problem. Collection and utilisation of energy perhaps is a problem. Producing a "greenhouse" layer of gases in the Earth's atmosphere to trap all the heat perhaps is a problem. Increasing the level of warming by burning and degrading resources to heat is possibly a problem too. You are the generation that may find out for sure!!

Fossil Fuel Power Production

It may be surprising to you, with all the focus these days on global warming and "greener fuels" that over three quarters of world energy production still comes from the burning of fossil fuels. The reasons are largely historical and geographical. Industrialisation led to a hugely increased rate of energy usage and industries were developed near to large deposits of fossil fuels.

If you do some internet research you will see many arguments suggesting that energy usage and power station efficiencies have not changed significantly over the last several decades and that this has much to do with short term economy and profit. The next decade or two will be very interesting times in seeing what changes are made and what new energy technologies are developed.

Using Energy Densities to calculate rate of fuel consumption

The following table shows approximate energy density figures for various fuels:

Fuel	Energy Density ($MJkg^{-1}$)
natural gas	50
crude oil	45
coal	25
water in a dam (100m high)	0.001
Uranium-235 (nuclear power)	88.25×10^6

Example T8.1

Find the mass per day of each of the above "fuels" that would be needed to output a power of 400MW (a fairly typical value for a power station)

Clearly, energy density of fuels is an important factor to consider when choosing a suitable fuel for a power station.

Power Station Efficiencies

The figures are similar for all three types of power station: Approximate maximum efficiencies are:

Coal fired power stations: 42%
Oil fired power stations: 45%
Natural gas fired stations: 52%

Typical power stations may run at between 5 and 10% lower than these efficiencies.
Environmental Problems associated with fossil fuel use in Power Stations

Pollution (acid rain, greenhouse gases), damaged environment when extracting, pollution when transporting large masses of fuels to power stations (increased traffic), non-renewable so will eventually run out

Non-fossil fuel power production

Nuclear Power

Overview

Nuclear power is the power associated with energy produced as a result of nuclear reactions.

When a nuclear reaction takes place an enormous amount of heat energy may be liberated (given out) so nuclear power is potentially very useful.

Nuclear reactions, unlike chemical reactions, involve nuclear changes. Atoms, thus, are not conserved. Total mass number and total proton number, however, are conserved (after the reaction, compared with before the reaction).

There are two kinds of nuclear reactions: nuclear fusion and nuclear fission. Fusion is where two light nuclei come together to form a heavy nucleus. Fission is where a heavy nucleus breaks apart to form two (or more) lighter nuclei.

The Nuclear Fission Power Plant (Power Station)

A nuclear fission power plant works essentially in the same way as a fossil fuel power plant, as discussed earlier. The key difference is the fuel that is used to produce the heat.

Some important terms:

- **(Nuclear) Chain reaction** – a nuclear reaction that causes one or more other nuclear reactions to take place.

- **Fissionable** – a fissionable material is one that can undergo nuclear fission

- **Fissile** – a fissile material is one that can undergo nuclear fission (is fissionable) by neutrons with low kinetic energy

- **Isotopes** – two or more nuclei with the same atomic number but different atomic masses. Uranium 235 and uranium 238 are isotopes of uranium. Most naturally occurring elements occur as a mixture of more than one isotope.

Fuel

The fuel in a nuclear fission power plant must be able to sustain itself: once the reaction is started it must be able to continue on its own (i.e. we must have a chain reaction). If high energy neutrons (very fast) are targeted at uranium 238 nuclei, they undergo fission. However, the extra neutrons produced are quite slow and do not have enough energy to cause further fission reactions with uranium 238. Hence uranium 238 is fissionable but not fissile.

However, uranium 235 is different. When a U-235 nucleus is bombarded with a low energy neutron, it undergoes fission to produce more low energy neutrons and lots of thermal energy. Uranium 235 is fissile. It is the only relatively abundant naturally occurring fissile isotope.

Enrichment

Naturally occurring uranium contains only about 0.7% uranium 235, the required isotope for power plant chain reactions. The remainder is mainly uranium 238, the non-fissile isotope. Enrichment is the process whereby the quantity of uranium 235 in a sample of natural uranium is increased. The remaining uranium 238 after enrichment is called depleted uranium. Countries that have nuclear power capabilities have the ability to easily further enrich uranium to concentrations sufficient to produce nuclear bombs – so these countries must be considered to also have nuclear weapon capability.

The chain reaction – Diagram showing the mechanism for a possible fission chain reaction:

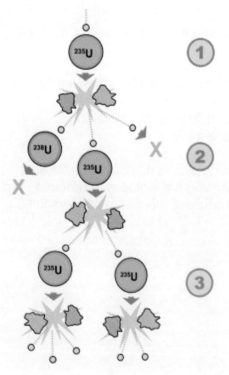

1. A uranium 235 atom (nucleus) absorbs a neutron and causes it to fission into two fission fragments (smaller daughter nuclei) and to release 3 new neutrons along with a large amount of thermal energy

2. One of the 3 neutrons released collides with a uranium 238 nucleus. But Uranium 238 nuclei are not fissile so this nucleus does not release further neutrons. Another neutron escapes without being absorbed. However the third of the released neutrons collides with another uranium 235 nucleus. It splits into two fission fragments and two additional neutrons and also releases more thermal energy.

3. Both of the released neutrons collide with uranium 235 nuclei so even more energy is released, along with further fission fragments and more neutrons.

Note that usually two or three neutrons are released after each fission. Studying this diagram, one can see that there is the chance that all released nuclei are absorbed by uranium 238 or escape the material without collisions. If this happens, then the reaction is not sustained and we have only a very short lived chain reaction.

Critical chain reaction and critical mass

A critical chain reaction is one which sustains itself. For a nuclear plant to work we must have critical chain reactions taking place. The chance of achieving this is increased by increasing the concentration of uranium 235 (enriching), by reducing the speed of the nuclei released and by increasing the mass of uranium present. The mass of uranium required to achieve a self sustaining chain reaction is called the **critical mass**. The critical mass of uranium 235 is a mass about the size of a grapefruit.

Moderation / Moderators

As stated, slowing down the neutrons will increase the chance of achieving a critical chain reaction. This is because slowing down the neutrons increases the chance of them causing fission when they collide with a uranium atom. The material used for this slowing down process is called a moderator. Regular water is the most commonly used moderator.

Control Rods

If the chain reaction is left as it is, more and more neutrons cause more fissions and the chain reaction becomes uncontrolled. The heat produced is then explosive. Such chain reactions are how fission bombs work. Control rods are used to control fission chain reactions. Control rods simply absorb neutrons. So if the reaction is going too fast, control rods are inserted into the reactor to absorb more neutrons. If the reaction is going too slow, they are removed. Control rods can be made of many different materials. One example is boron.

Nuclear Reactor

A nuclear reactor is a device that contains, initiates and controls nuclear chain reactions at a steady and sustained rate. The purpose of a nuclear reactor is to convert nuclear energy into thermal energy (heat).

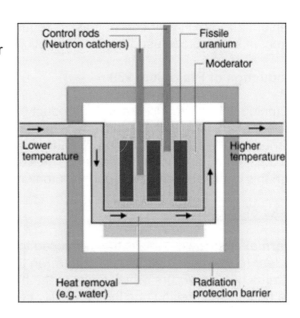

The diagram on the right (credit: European Nuclear Society) shows a schematic (simplified) view of a nuclear reactor.

Schematic Diagram of a Nuclear Power Station

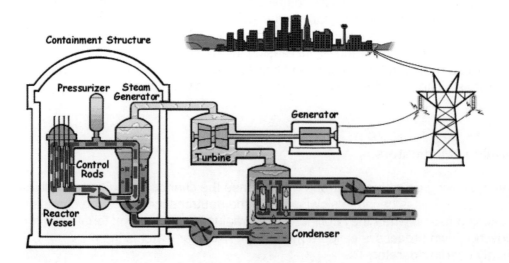

(Credit: http://www.nrc.gov/reading-rm/basic-ref/students/animated-pwr.html)

The reactor has already been discussed. Its purpose is to generate heat. The heat exchanger transfers heat away from the reactor. The heat is used to produce high pressure steam which then drives a turbine. The turbine is connected to a generator which converts this energy into electricity.

In the diagram above, the condenser converts the used and cooled steam back into water so it can be circulated again.

Plutonium 239

This is another fuel used in nuclear reactors. It has a higher probability for fission that uranium 235, so a lower critical mass is required. Plutonium 239 (Pu – 239) is the primary fissile isotope used for the production of nuclear weapons.

Production of Plutonium 239

Plutonium 239 is produced as a by-product of a collision with uranium 238, in the nuclear reactors already discussed. When a neutron strikes a U-238 atom, there is a chance of this reaction occurring. So there will be a significant amount of Pu-239 in the "spent fuel" of a uranium reactor. The Pu-239 can easily be chemically separated from this material to give high purity plutonium 239 metal.

Risks of Nuclear Power

Thermal meltdown – this is the term used to describe a severe nuclear accident. A nuclear (or thermal) meltdown occurs when the reaction is not controlled properly and extreme heating occurs, which leads to the highly reactive fission products becoming overheated and melting and the possibility of containment failure. There have been several nuclear meltdowns in history, the most famous being the Chernobyl disaster in 1986. Due to cover-ups, it is not known how many died, but the overall cost of the disaster is estimated at 200 billion US dollars; the costliest disaster in modern history.

Radioactive nuclear waste – remains radioactive for millions of years. often buried in geologically secure sites.

Dangers of mining and transporting radioactive materials (uranium) – mining is already dangerous. This has the added danger associated with radioactive materials.

Risk of inappropriate use for nuclear weapons

Nuclear Fusion Power

If we could harness the energy of nuclear fusion, this would produce safe products, since fusion reactions are between light nuclei and results in the production of another light and radioactively inactive nucleus.

The problem with this kind of power is that such extremely high temperatures are required to initiate a fusion reaction and it is very difficult to maintain and confine a high temperature, high density plasma that would be produced.

Solar Power

Solar power is harnessed in two possible ways: using photovoltaic cells ("solar cells") or using solar panels.

Photovoltaic cells convert light energy (sun's radiation) into electrical energy. This form of energy collection requires a large surface area for a relatively small amount of electrical energy. Solar cells, therefore, are commonly used to power smaller devices or the electrical energy produced can be fed into the grid system.

Solar heating panels (solar thermal collectors) convert light energy (sun's radiation) into thermal energy (heat). Solar heating panels are used increasingly on house roofs to assist in the heating of water for central heating and washing use.

Regional variations in solar power

Solar energy arriving at the Earth does so with an average power of approximately 1400 joules per second per square metre of the cross section of the beam ($1400 Wm^{-2}$)

However, as the diagram below shows, the power intensity is less than this when the sunlight does not strike the Earth's surface straight on. The same energy is spread over a large land area. Generally, the further from the equator, the less intense the power.

Additionally, a beam of radiation from the sun has to travel though a greater thickness of the Earth's atmosphere when it is further from the equator. Since radiation is partially absorbed by the Earth's atmosphere, the intensity is weakened when it reaches the Earth's surface – and to a greater extent as you move further from the equator.

Diagram showing how sunlight intensity at surface of Earth varies with position

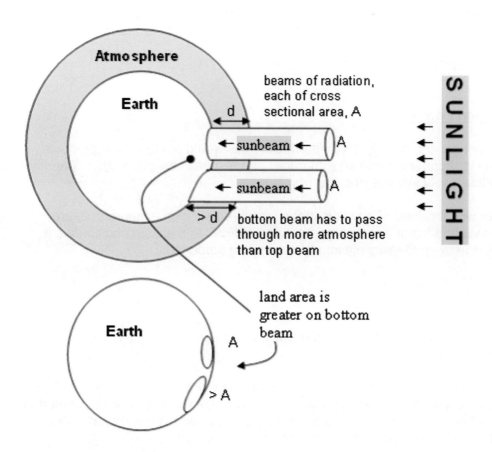

Hydroelectric Power

Hydroelectric power is power derived from gravitational potential energy of water: so, when water flows downwards, the gravitational potential energy is released and may be converted into electrical energy.

Energy Chain:

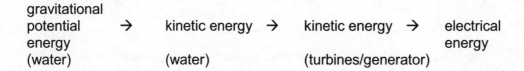

gravitational potential energy (water) → kinetic energy (water) → kinetic energy (turbines/generator) → electrical energy

Hydroelectric power is the most widely used renewable energy resource. In 2005, hydroelectric power produced 19% of the world's electricity.

It is a clean and free fuel. Emissions are (usually) clean. Running costs and maintenance are low.

On the other hand, dam construction can damage the environment and enormous quantities of methane gas (a potent greenhouse gas) can be produced by rotting vegetation when an area of land is flooded. Population relocation can be socially unjust and there is always a risk of dam failure: a big safety hazard.

You need to be aware of three different hydroelectric schemes:

Water storage in lakes and dams – the stored water can then be released, dropping to a lower level and, as it does, passing through turbines connected to generators and producing electricity.

Tidal water storage – water is trapped at high tide then released via turbines etc. once the tide drops.

Pump storage – water is pumped from a low reservoir to a high reservoir. The idea is that the pumping occurs at low demand periods, ready to provide extra power in times of demand. Clearly this method is not energy efficient, since at least as much (and in fact more) energy is required to pump the water up than is released when it falls back down.

Wind Power

Wind turbines like the one below essentially convert the kinetic energy of the wind into electrical energy. Note, though, that in accordance with the laws of thermodynamics, one can never convert all the energy from wind into mechanical, then electrical energy.

Construction/workings of a typical wind turbine.

A mechanism (called a "yaw") directs the turbine so that it optimises wind energy into mechanical energy in the turbines. Another mechanism stops the turbine and directs it away from the wind to prevent damage if the wind is too strong. The gearbox increases the rotation speed of the generator, maximising efficiency of mechanical → electrical energy conversion. The generator is also housed with the gearbox, inside the "Nacelle"

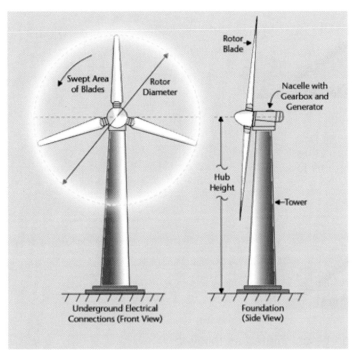

Credit ESN

If the windspeed of air passing through the turbine blades is known, you can easily calculate the maximum power delivery of a wind turbine, as follows:

$$m \,/\, second = \rho V \,/\, second = \rho \pi r^2 v \qquad (m \,/\, second = \text{mass of air per second})$$

(ρ = density of air, r = turbine radius)

(v = windspeed)

$$
\begin{aligned}
\text{Maximum Power available} \quad &= \tfrac{1}{2}(m \,/\, second)v^2 \\
&= \tfrac{1}{2}(\rho \pi r^2 v)v^2 \\
&= \tfrac{1}{2}\rho \pi r^2 v^3
\end{aligned}
$$

Wave Power

Wave power converts wave energy (essentially kinetic energy) into electrical energy. An oscillating water column (OWC) is a device that captures wave energy, converting it into electrical energy.

Oscillating Water Column (OWC)

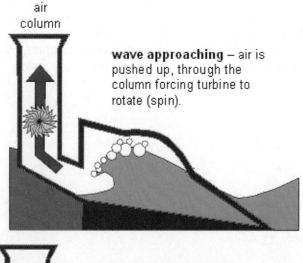

air column

wave approaching – air is pushed up, through the column forcing turbine to rotate (spin).

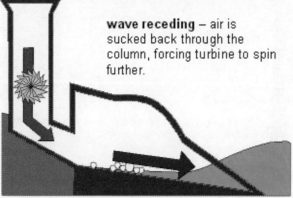

wave receding – air is sucked back through the column, forcing turbine to spin further.

The energy delivery of a wave can be calculated as follows:

Power per metre-width of wave $= \dfrac{\rho g A^2 v}{2}$ (equation in data book)

where:

$\rho = water\ density,\ \ g = gravity,\ \ A = wave\ amplitude,\ \ v = wave-speed$

Greenhouse Effect

Solar radiation

The sun emits radiation from the whole of the electromagnetic spectrum (gamma rays, X-rays, Ultraviolet, Visible and Infrared). However, the atmosphere filters out many wavelengths and ultraviolet, visible and infra red radiation are the three main types of radiation reaching the Earth's surface.

The amount (intensity) of radiation reaching the surface of any planet can easily be calculated using the "inverse square law", but we would need to assume negligible radiation absorption by the atmosphere – which may not always be realistic.

Inverse square law

$$I = \frac{power}{area}\ (in\ data\ book) = \frac{P}{4\pi r^2}$$

where I is the intensity at a distance r from the point source

Example T8.2

Given that the intensity of the sun at the surface of the Earth (the solar constant) is about $1400\,Wm^{-2}$ and that the Earth is approximately 150 million kilometres from the Earth:

    (a) find an approximate value for the power of the sun
    (b) find the approximate intensity at the surface of Jupiter, given that Jupiter is
        approximately 780 million kilometres from the sun.

To calculate how much energy a planet actually receives of course you would need to take into account filtration and reflection of radiation by the planet's atmosphere.

Also, the surface of a planet will reflect some of the radiation straight back into space.

Albedo

The ability of a planet to reflect radiation back is called albedo. The Earth's albedo varies significantly depending on season (colours) and surface: snow (being white and shiny), for example has a high albedo, whereas oceans have low albedos.

Albedo – definition: the proportion of power (or energy) reflected compared to the total power (or energy) received.

Equation: $albedo = \dfrac{total\ scattered\ power}{total\ incident\ power}$ (given in data book)

The albedo of snowy surfaces, for example, is about 0.85 – indicating that this type of surface reflects 85% of the sun's radiation back. The global annual mean albedo of the Earth is 0.3 (so approximately 70% of the radiation reaching the sun is absorbed by the Earth.

The greenhouse effect

The greenhouse effect is the warming effect that the atmosphere has on the earth.

To understand the greenhouse effect, we first need to understand that the Earth is always absorbing energy from the sun and it is also always emitting radiation. All bodies possessing thermal energy emit radiation. The type of radiation emitted depends on the temperature of the body. The Earth emits mainly infrared radiation.

The greenhouse warming effect occurs because some gases in the atmosphere are able to absorb infrared radiation emitted from the Earth. As the gases increase in temperature, they then begin to emit radiation. However, they emit radiation in all directions, so some of the energy is sent back to Earth. Hence warming occurs.

Greenhouse gases are gases that easily absorb infrared radiation. Examples include carbon dioxide, water vapour, methane and nitrous oxide. These gases all have bonds that oscillate with the same range of frequencies as part of the infra-red range of frequencies. They are therefore able to absorb energy by a process known as resonance (the driving frequency, infrared radiation) is the same as the natural frequency as the oscillator being driven (the greenhouse gases)).

Black Body Radiation

A "black body" absorbs all radiation that falls on it and reflects none; hence it is black (reflects no light) when it is cold.

However, when a black body is hot it emits radiation. If it is at the same temperature as the surroundings it will emit exactly as much radiation as it absorbs and at every wavelength. So, (hot) black bodies always emit radiation at all wavelengths.

The relative proportions of radiation emitted depend on the temperature of the body.

The following diagram shows the emission spectra of black bodies at different temperatures:

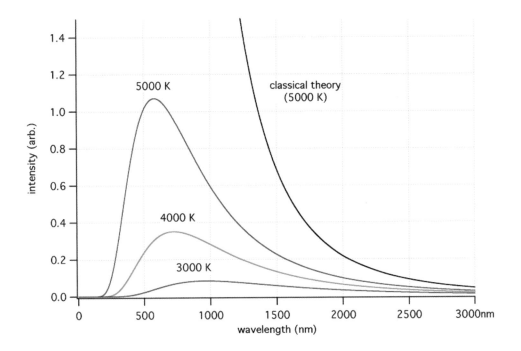

As the temperature increases, the peak intensity moves to higher intensity and shorter wavelength.

The theory of black body radiation explains and can be used to predict the colour of very hot objects. A heated metal, for example, first appears red hot, then white hot (at very high temperatures) this colour corresponds to the peak intensity on the above diagram.

Most objects at "everyday Earth" temperatures emit radiation mostly in the infrared region of the spectrum – so the peak would be in the infrared region in above diagram.

Stefan-Boltzmann Law

This law links the total power emitted (radiated) by a body to its temperature, in the following equation:

For a black body: $power = \sigma A T^4$ (given in data book)

For any body: $power = e\sigma A T^4$ (given in data book)

where: σ = Stefan-Boltzmann constant = $5.67 \times 10^{-8} Wm^{-2}K^{-4}$
       A = surface area of the emitter
       T = absolute (Kelvin) temperature of the emitter
       e = the emissivity of the surface

Emissivity

The emissivity is a number (from 0 to 1) measuring of how well a surface emits radiation. Good emitters have emissivities close to 1 (A perfect emitter, a black body, has an emissivity equal to 1).

Example T8.3

Find the approximate radiation power of the Sun and the Earth, given the following data:

Radius of Sun:	$7.0 \times 10^8 m$
Radius of Earth:	$6.4 \times 10^6 m$
Surface temperature of Sun:	$5800K$
Surface temperature of the Earth:	25°C

(Surface area = $4\pi r^2$, assume $e(Earth) = 0.7$ and $e(sun) = 0.95$)

Surface Heat Capacity

Surface heat capacity is a measurement of how much energy is required to heat up 1 m² of a surface by 1°C (or 1 K). It is therefore measured in $Jm^{-2}K^{-1}$.

Equation: $C_s = \dfrac{Q}{A\Delta T}$

where: C_s =surface heat capacity, Q = energy, A =land area, ΔT =temperature difference

Example T8.4

Find an approximate value for the surface heat capacity of Lake Zug (Switzerland) given that the average radiation intensity is approximately $300\ Wm^{-2}$, that the surface area of the lake is approximately $38km^2$ and that it takes 3 weeks for the lake to warm up by 2°C.

Global Warming

Global warming is the term we use to describe the recent trend that the Earth's temperature is increasing.

Global surface temperature (oceans and near-surface air) has increased by approximately 0.75°C in the last one hundred years. Whilst this may not seem alarming, it is worth noting that small affects can lead to larger effects (as described later) and that predictions show that there is little we can do to prevent continued increases.

Enhanced Greenhouse effect

There is evidence to show that there have been large fluctuations in global temperatures before humans inhabited the Earth. Indeed, the presence of the atmosphere in its natural state has a greenhouse effect.

Many people (including scientists) believe that the recent global warming trends are a result of human activity and that we need to change some of these activities.

The enhanced greenhouse effect is the expression used to describe the greenhouse effect due to human activities.

Possible causes of enhanced greenhouse effect (and global warming)

- increased burning of fossil fuels
- deforestation
- increased pollution upsetting the chemical balance of the atmosphere
- increased energy consumption

Evidence to link global warming to increased level of greenhouse gases

ice-core research - drilling cores of ice, age of ice increases with depth. Composition of ice gives information about atmospheric composition (trapped air in bubbles) and temperatures (structure of ice). Ice-core drilling has revealed information from up to 420000 years ago. This evidence shows that there is a strong link between global temperatures and the quantity of CO_2 in the atmosphere.

Some Mechanisms

Ice/snow melting – global warming causes ice and snow to melt. This reduces the albedo of the surface so less radiation is reflected back to space, so more thermal energy is absorbed by the Earth.

Solubility of CO_2 in sea water decreases as the temperature increases. This, in turn, leads to greater atmospheric concentrations of CO_2, which leads to further global warming.

Deforestation – not only causes CO_2 release (when burned) but trees take up CO_2 (by photosynthesis) "fixing" the carbon in starch (i.e. the wood). Less trees means less carbon fixing and more in the atmosphere

Coefficient of Volume Expansion

The coefficient of volume expansion is the fractional change in volume per unit (°C or K) change in temperature.

This measurement has relevance with global warming since we can calculate the expansions of the oceans caused by an increase in temperature.

For water, this coefficient changes as the temperature of water changes. As the temperature of water is increased from 0 to 4°C water actually decreases in volume. Also ice is less dense than liquid water (water is unusual in this respect). Water behaves in a more conventional manner at temperatures above 4 °C, expanding as its temperature increases.

Add these complications to the complexity of ice in water and ice on land (does a melt, then, cause an increase or a decrease in water heights?) and you have some complicated calculations. Current predictions project significant sea level rises over the next 50-100 years.

Possible Suggestions to reduce the enhanced greenhouse effect

- **greater efficiency of power production**, leading to less energy degradation and less greenhouse gas emissions

- **replacing the use of coal and oil with natural gas** – coal and oil effectively fix carbon (it cannot escape into atmosphere unless fuel is burned). Natural gas power also tends to be more efficient than coal/oil.

- **Increased use of combined heating and power (CHP) systems** – this is where power stations make use of excess heat instead of releasing it into the atmosphere. The effective use of the heat (for example to heat homes or factories) then means less power demand from the grid system and other power stations. Overall efficiency is increased.

- **Increased use of renewable energy resources** – that way, carbon is continually recycled rather than continually released into the atmosphere (as it is with fossil fuel combustion)

- **Increased use of nuclear power** – no greenhouse gas emission (but other safety issues)

- **Carbon dioxide capture and storage** – rather than releasing CO_2 into the atmosphere when fossil fuels are burned, it could be collected and used (for example, in brewing industry or for greenhouses)

- **Use of hybrid vehicles** – replace diesel and petrol engines with hybrids (run on electricity or fuel).

- **Reforestation** – so that carbon can be fixed via plant photosynthesis

International Efforts

If the enhanced greenhouse effect is indeed a real threat to our future livelihoods it is pointless for one country to make take action if others do not. Climate and air mass is shared and the environment is not possible to divide up into safe and unsafe places: international action and cooperation is necessary.

There are various international initiatives to reduce the enhanced greenhouse effect. Examples include:

- **Intergovernmental Panel on Climate Change (IPCC)** – regularly assesses current evidence from international research

- **The Kyoto Protocol** – Part of the United Nations: a treaty agreeing certain measures to reduce the enhanced greenhouse effect. Countries can sign the protocol. If they do not (e.g. USA and Australia, currently) there is increased international political pressure to do so.

- **Asia-Pacific Partnership on Clean Development and Climate (APPCDC)** – an agreement between Australia, China, India, Japan, Korea and the USA (representing 50% of world's energy users) to make efforts to consider climate change and pollution reduction, amongst other things, with a view to promoting sustainable economic growth and poverty reduction.

Solutions to SL Section Problems

Topic 1: Physics and Physical Measurement

Example T1.1

Quantity	Usual Symbol	Unit	F/D	V/S
Mass	m	kg	F	S
Length	l	m	F	S
Time	t	s	F	S
Current	I	A	F	S
Temperature	T	K	F	S
Force	F	N	D	V
Displacement	s	m	F	V
Speed	v	ms^{-1}	D	S
Acceleration	a	ms^{-2}	D	V
Pressure	P	Pa	D	S
Potential difference	V	V	D	S
Resistance	R	Ω	D	S
Energy	E or Q	J	D	S
Charge	q	C	D	S
Velocity	v	ms^{-1}	D	V
Power	p	W	D	S
Frequency	f	Hz	D	S

Example T1.2

units of kWh = units of power(kW) × units of time(h)

$\qquad$ = watts × seconds

$\qquad$ = $joules/_{seconds}$ × seconds

$\qquad$ = joules

(showing that the kWh is equivalent to a joule)

units of the joule:
using work = force × distance, and force = mass × acceleration,
units of J = N×m = kg×ms^{-2}×m = kgm^{2}s^{-2}

so the kWh and the joule are derived from the base units: kgm^{2}s^{-2}

Example T1.3

conversion to S.I. units (using scientific notation)
$300 \times 10^{-9} m = 3 \times 10^{-7} m$
$0.6 \times 10^{-6} s = 6 \times 10^{-7} s$
$500 \times 10^{-3} V = 0.5 V$
$0.3 \times 10^{-2} m = 3 \times 10^{-3} m$
$101 \times 10^{3} Pa = 1.01 \times 10^{5} Pa$
$23.4 \times 10^{6} N = 2.34 \times 10^{7} N$

Example T1.4

(a)

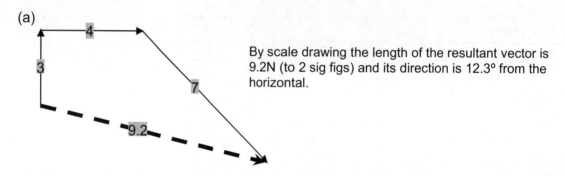

By scale drawing the length of the resultant vector is 9.2N (to 2 sig figs) and its direction is 12.3° from the horizontal.

Note that you are not expected to get the exact answer, but are expected to draw a neat, accurate scale drawing and get an answer close to the correct value.

(b)

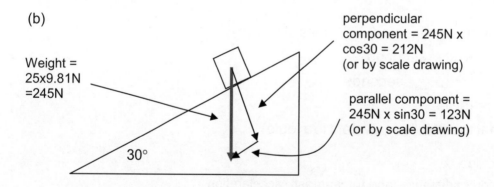

Weight = 25x9.81N =245N

30°

perpendicular component = 245N x cos30 = 212N (or by scale drawing)

parallel component = 245N x sin30 = 123N (or by scale drawing)

(c)   The resultant *speed* is the *length* of vector that is the vector sum of the two component velocities (speeds & directions) given.

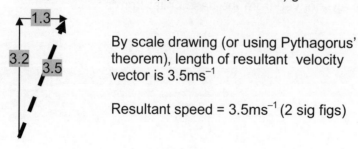

By scale drawing (or using Pythagorus' theorem), length of resultant velocity vector is 3.5ms^{-1}

Resultant speed = 3.5ms^{-1} (2 sig figs)

Topic 2: Mechanics

Example T2.1

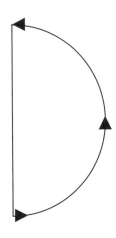

$$Av.\ speed = \frac{dist.traveled}{time\ taken} = \frac{\frac{1}{2} \times 2\pi r}{3.5} = 10.8\ (ms^{-1})$$

Speed after 1s = 10.8ms^{-1}

$$Av.velocity = \frac{displ.}{time} = \frac{24m}{3.5s} = 6.86ms^{-1}, due\ north$$

Velocity after 1s = 10.8ms^{-1} at a direction given by the tangent to the circle at that point (the direction at which it is traveling)

Note that actual (instantaneous) velocity is equal to the instantaneous speed and instantaneous direction.

Example T2.2

graph	displacement		velocity		acceleration	
	sign	change	sign	change	sign	change
A	+	con	0	con	0	con
B	+	inc	+	con	0	con
C	+	inc	+	inc	+	cannot tell – can only tell that velocity is inc
D	+	dec	–	con	0	con
E	–	inc	+	con	0	con
F	+	inc	+	con	0	con
G	+	inc	+	inc	+	con
H	+	inc	+	inc	+	inc
I	+	inc	+	dec	–	con
J	–	dec	–	inc	+	con
K	+	inc	+	inc	+	con
L	+	inc	+	inc	+	inc
M	+	inc	+	inc	+	inc
N	+	inc	+	inc	+	dec
O	–	dec	-	dec	–	inc

Example T2.3

acceleration $= gradient$

$$= \frac{(v-u)}{t} \quad \Rightarrow a = \frac{(v-u)}{t} \Rightarrow at = v - u \Rightarrow v = u + at$$

*Equation*1: $\quad v = u + at$

displacement $= area\ under\ graph = \frac{1}{2}(u+v) \times t \Rightarrow s = \frac{(u+v)}{2}t$

*Equation*2: $\quad s = \frac{(u+v)}{2}t$

Eliminate *v* *from Equation*1 *and* 2 (*substitute*(1) *into* (2)):

$$s = \frac{(u+(u+at))}{2}t = \frac{(2u+at)}{2}t = (u + \tfrac{1}{2}at)t = ut + \tfrac{1}{2}at^2$$

∴

*Equation*3: $\quad s = ut + \tfrac{1}{2}at^2$

Eliminate *t* *from Equation*1 *and* 2 :

from (1): $\quad t = \frac{(v-u)}{a}$

from (2): $\quad s = ut + \tfrac{1}{2}at^2 = u\left(\frac{(v-u)}{a}\right) + \tfrac{1}{2}a\left(\frac{(v-u)}{a}\right)^2$

$$= \frac{uv - u^2}{a} + \frac{(v^2 - 2uv + u^2)}{2a} = \frac{(2uv - 2u^2 + v^2 - 2uv + u^2)}{2a} = \frac{(v^2 - u^2)}{2a}$$

$$\Rightarrow s = \frac{(v^2 - u^2)}{2a} \Rightarrow 2as = v^2 - u^2 \Rightarrow 2as + u^2 = v^2$$

∴ *Equation* 4: $\quad v^2 = u^2 + 2as$

Example T2.4

(a) Considering the motion from point of projection to highest point:

$u = 25, \ v = 0, \ a = -9.81$ (*taking upwards as positive*)
$s = we\ need\ to\ find$

Using $v^2 = u^2 + 2as$
$0 = 25^2 + 2(-9.81)s \Rightarrow 625 = 19.62s \Rightarrow s = 31.86$

Answer : *Height* $= 31.9m$

(b) Considering the motion from point of projection to point where it hits ground

$u = 25, \ s = 0, \ a = -9.81, \ t = ? \, (\textit{to find})$

Using $s = ut + \frac{1}{2}at^2$

$0 = 25t + \frac{1}{2}(-9.81)t^2 \Rightarrow t = 5.10s \ (\textit{by quadratic formula})$

Example T2.5

Of course the iron ball would hit the ground first! However, if air resistance is ignored the only force acting is the weight of the objects. Using F=ma and the force, F(weight) = mg, we get $a = \frac{F}{m} = \frac{mg}{m} = g = 9.81$ (the ratio of any weight to its mass is the same, g.

So if air resistance is ignored both objects have equal accelerations, and so would hit the ground at the same time.

In reality air resistance is significant (compared to downward force – weight) in the case of low density objects so the equations of motion do not apply.

Not only is it more complicated in such cases to find the resultant force acting on objects, but air resistance increases as speed increases so acceleration is not uniform. The equations of motion therefore cannot be used to accurately determine the motion of falling objects under the influence of significant air resistance

Examples T2.6

1) woman on the floor

↑ normal reaction (from floor)

⊕

↓ weight (due to gravity)

note that these forces are equal (in size) and opposite (in direction)

2) man falling through the air, ignore air resistance

⊖

↓ weight (due to gravity)

3) A mass sliding down frictionless slope

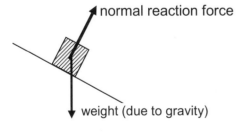

normal reaction force

weight (due to gravity)

Note that the resultant of these two forces is a force parallel to the slope (acting down the slope) so the lengths should ideally correspond to this idea.

4) parachutist falling at terminal speed

air resistance

weight (due to gravity)

note that these forces are
equal (in size) and
opposite (in direction)
since acceleration = 0

Example T2.7

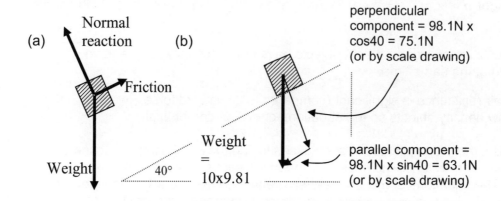

(a) Normal reaction   (b)

Friction

Weight

Weight = 10x9.81

40°

perpendicular
component = 98.1N x
cos40 = 75.1N
(or by scale drawing)

parallel component =
98.1N x sin40 = 63.1N
(or by scale drawing)

(c)   The three forces shown on the free-body diagram must all add up
(vectorially) to zero (since the mass is motionless and therefore has
zero acceleration). Normal reaction cancels component of weight that
is perpendicular to slope, and friction cancels component of weight
parallel to slope. Therefore, frictional force = 63.1N, acting parallel to
the slope, upwards

Example T2.8

Motion	Displacement	Velocity	Acceleration	Force
Immediately after thrown	+ (close to 0)	+	–	–
Half - way up	+	+	–	–
At highest point	+	0	–	–
Half - way down	+	–	–	–
just before hits ground	+ (but very close to 0)	–	–	–

Example T2.9

If the slope were frictionless, the free-body diagram would
look like the diagram shown on the right.

Since the object does not accelerate up or down, in a
direction perpendicular, the normal reaction force has to
cancel out the component of the weight perpendicular to
the slope.

The only force left is the component of the weight parallel to

the slope – and this is no surprise, since we know intuitively
that the mass accelerates down the slope, in the direction of the slope

Therefore resultant force = 63.1N (see T2.7)

$F = ma \Rightarrow a = \frac{F}{m} = \frac{63.1}{10} = 6.31 \quad \therefore acceleration = 6.31ms^{-2}$

Example T2.10

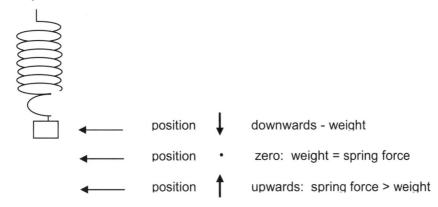

position	↓	downwards - weight
position	•	zero: weight = spring force
position	↑	upwards: spring force > weight

Example T2.11

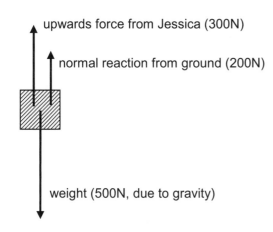

upwards force from Jessica (300N)

normal reaction from ground (200N)

weight (500N, due to gravity)

Note that since weight is not
accelerating, resultant force on
weight = 0

Pairs of equal & opposite forces:

300N applied on weight, by Jessica
300N applied on Jessica, by weight

200N applied on weight, by ground
200N applied on ground, by weight

500N applied on weight, by Earth
500N applied on Earth, by weight

Example T2.12

(a) *impulse = change in momentum = m(v − u)*
$\therefore 14,400 = 1200(v - 0)$
$\Rightarrow 1200v = 14,400 \quad \Rightarrow v = \frac{14400}{1200} = 12$
Answer : $12ms^{-1}$
(b) $F = ma = 1200 \times 0.8 = 960 \quad$ *Answer* : $960N$

(c) *impulse = Ft* $\quad \therefore 14400 = 960t \Rightarrow t = \frac{14400}{960} = 15$
Answer : $15s$

Example T2.13

Example Method:

Total momentum before = total momentum after collision

$\therefore \quad 0.02 \times 3 + 0.02 \times -3 = 0.02 \times -1 + 0.02v$

$\Rightarrow 0 = -0.02 + 0.02v \Rightarrow 0.02v = 0.02 \Rightarrow v = 1$

kinetic energy before $= \frac{1}{2}(0.02)(3)^2 + \frac{1}{2}(0.02)(-3)^2 = 0.18J$

kinetic energy after $= \frac{1}{2}(0.02)(-1)^2 + \frac{1}{2}(0.02)(1)^2 = 0.02J$

$\therefore$ *partially elastic (particles would stick together if totally inelastic)*

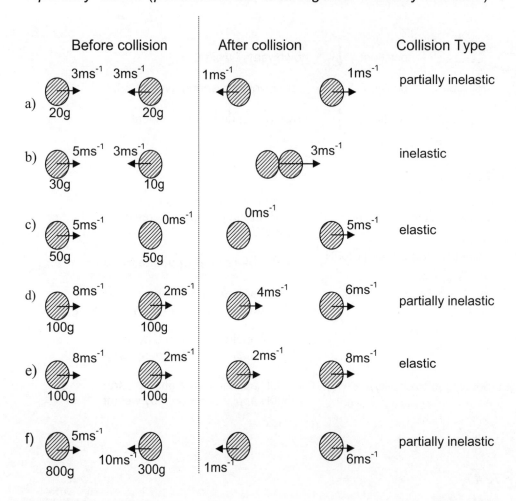

Example T2.14

a) work done by pump
 = electrical energy converted to other forms
 = electrical power x time
 = 2000 x 3 x 60 x 60
 = 21600000 J   =21.6MJ

b) Eg   = mg△h
 = 100 x 1000 x 9.81 x 5
 = 4905000J   = 4.91 MJ (to 3 sig. figs.)

c) efficiency $= \dfrac{\textit{useful work done}}{\textit{total energy used}} \times 100 = \dfrac{4905000}{21600000} \times 100$

 = 22.7%

Although 77.3% of the electrical energy has been wasted, the principal of conservation of energy still applies (as it always does). Energy is conserved. Some of the electrical energy is wasted: converted into heat in the water and surroundings produced by work done against friction and water resistance, and sound.

Example T2.15

The theoretical work done by the man is zero, since there is no overall movement in the direction of the force (weight or normal reaction), up or down. No energy is required to keep a mass moving at a constant velocity (so no change in kinetic energy), and at the same height (so no change in gravitational potential energy). In reality the man would have to work, and therefore use up energy. This is because of resistance to motion.

Example T2.16

(a)

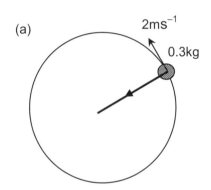

Force needed to keep mass in circle

$$= \frac{mv^2}{r}$$

Tension is the only force acting in the plane of motion (horizontal)

$$\therefore T = \frac{mv^2}{r} = \frac{0.3 \times 2^2}{0.25} = 4.8N$$

(b)

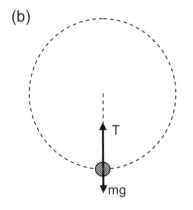

Resultant force = T − mg

$$\therefore \frac{mv^2}{r} = T\text{-mg}$$

$$\Rightarrow T = \frac{mv^2}{r} + mg$$

$$= \frac{0.3 x 4}{0.25} + 0.3 x 9.81$$

$$\Rightarrow T = 7.74 \text{ N (to 3 sig. figs.)}$$

Tension will be the smallest at the highest point (where the weight actually contributes towards centripetal force, and will be maximum at the lowest position. Assuming that speed is constant, resultant force (centripetal force) is therefore taken to be constant.

Topic 3: Thermal Physics

Example T3.1

$$c = \frac{27000}{(3 \times 12)} = 750 \quad Answer: 750 J/kg/°C \ (750 Jkg^{-1}°C^{-1})$$

Example T3.2

$$c = \frac{10500}{(0.5 \times 5)} = 4200 \quad Answer: 4200 Jkg^{-1}°C^{-1}$$

Example T3.3

$$Q = mc\Delta T$$
$$= 7.5 \times 2100 \times 13 = 204750 \quad Answer: 205 KJ \ (to \ 3 \ significant \ figures)$$

Example T3.4

$$(a) \ c = \frac{Q}{\Delta T} = \frac{1.66 \times 10^6}{(21-9)} = 138333.33$$

The heat capacity of the oven is 1.38x10^5 JK^{-1} (or 1.38x105 $J°C^{-1}$)

$$(b) \ c = \frac{C}{m} = \frac{138333}{220} = 628.786$$

The specific heat capacity of the material is 629 $Jkg^{-1}K^{-1}$

Example T3.5

$$Q = ml \Rightarrow l = \frac{Q}{m} = \frac{1700000}{5} = 340000 \quad Answer: 3.4 \times 10^5 \ Jkg^{-1}$$

Example T3.6

$$Q = ml = 0.5 \times 2.26 \times 10^6 = 1.13 \times 10^6 \quad Answer: \ 1.13 MJ$$

Example T3.7

$$pV = nRT \Rightarrow n = \frac{PV}{RT} = \frac{101 \times 10^3 \times (0.25 \times 0.50 \times 0.50)}{8.31 \times (273 + 25)} = 2.54908$$
$$mass = moles \times molar \ mass = 2.54908 \times 28 = 71.37$$

Answer: Mass of air is in container is approximately 71.4g

Topic 4: Oscillations and Waves

Example T4.1

(a) 5cm

(b) A movement of 20cm (back and forth) = 1 oscillation

Therefore period = $\frac{20}{50} \times 1.25 = 0.5s$

(c) $\omega = \frac{2\pi}{T} = \frac{2\pi}{0.5} = 4\pi rads^{-1}$ $(12.6 rads^{-1})$

(d) Max velocity is at position B, after 5cm, after $\frac{5}{50} \times 1.25s = 0.125s$

$v = \omega\sqrt{x_0^2 - x^2}$ but $x = o$, $x_0 = 0.05$ (*zero displacement at B*)

so $v = 4\pi\sqrt{0.05^2} = 0.63 ms^{-1}$

Note that, if we take B as the zero displacement position (sensible), then velocity is always maximum at this point and acceleration is always zero at this point. Then at maximum displacement (points A and C) velocity is zero and acceleration is maximum.

For (e) to (h) – we should assume time = 0 at zero displacment then use the equations: $x = x_0 \sin\omega t$; $v = v_0 \cos\omega t$; $a = -\omega^2 x$. Ensure that your calculator is in the correct MODE (radians)

(e) (At B, moving to right – take right as positive) $x = 0$, $v = 0.63 ms^{-1}$, $a = 0$

(f) (At C, not moving) $x = +5cm$, $v = 0$, $a = -\omega^2 x = -7.9 ms^{-2}$

(g) (At B, moving to left) $x = 0$, $v = -0.63 ms^{-1}$, $a = 0$

(h) (just to left of B, moving to right) We need to take
$t = 0.6 - 0.125 = 0.475s$ - the time after first passing zero displacement, C

$x = 0.05\sin(4\pi \times 0.475) = -0.015m = -1.5cm$

$v = 0.05\cos(4\pi \times 0.475) = +0.048 ms^{-1}$

$a = -\omega^2 x = +2.44 ms^{-2}$

Example T4.2

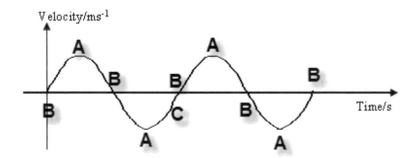

(c) Displacement is the area between the curve and the time axis

(d) Acceleration is the gradient of the curve at any particular time

(e) (i) Initially positive velocity and positive area, then negative, then positive – showing that velocity and displacement is "back and forth"

(ii) Maximum positive displacements (e.g. at 2nd B from left), shown by positive area corresponds to maximum negative acceleration (shown by negative gradient at this point) – this agrees with definition of simple harmonic motion ($a \; \alpha \; -x$)

(f) The displacement is found by taking the total area from start – we have an initial positive area followed by an equal but negative area – so total displacement at point C is zero.

Example T4.3

(a) gravitational PE → KE → GPE → KE etc.

(b) $E_{k(max)} = \dfrac{1}{2}m\omega^2 x_o^2 = 5.9\times10^{-3}J$

(c) $E_k = \dfrac{1}{2}m\omega^2(x_0^2 - x^2) = 3.8\times10^{-3}J$

(d) $E_k = \dfrac{1}{2}m\omega^2(x_0^2 - x^2) = 5.0\times10^{-3}J$

(e) 0.1 seconds after release corresponds to 0.025 seconds before zero displacement point – i.e. $t = -0.025s$

$x = x_0\sin(\omega t) = -0.0155m$

$E_k = \dfrac{1}{2}m\omega^2(x_0^2 - x^2) = 5.4\times10^{-3}J$

Example T4.4

(a) $v = f\lambda \Rightarrow f = \dfrac{v}{\lambda} = \dfrac{3.00\times10^8}{3.8\times10^{-13}} = 7.9\times10^{20}\,Hz$

(b) $v = f\lambda = 256\times1.3 = 333Hz$

(c) Either: $T = 0.8s$, $f = \dfrac{1}{T} = 1.25Hz$, $v = f\lambda = 1.25\times2.5 = 3.1ms^{-1}$

or: $speed = \dfrac{dist}{time} = \dfrac{1.25}{0.4} = 3.1ms^{-1}$

Example T4.5

For the EMS, frequency range $\approx \dfrac{3\times10^8}{10^{-15}}$ to $\dfrac{3\times10^8}{10} \approx 10^{23}\,Hz$ to $10^7\,Hz$

So, EMS has much greater range of frequency and much higher frequencies.

Example T4.6

(a) $c = \dfrac{\sin 47}{\sin 29} = 1.51$

(b) $1.51 = \dfrac{c_1}{c_2} = \dfrac{3\times10^8}{c_2} \Rightarrow c_2 = 2.0\times10^8\,ms^{-1}$

(c) $1.51 = \dfrac{\lambda_1}{\lambda_2} = \dfrac{\lambda_1}{600\times10^{-9}} \Rightarrow \lambda_1 = 9.05\times10^{-7}m \approx 900nm$

(d) $f = \dfrac{v}{\lambda} = \dfrac{3.0\times10^{8}}{9.05\times10^{-7}} = 3.3\times10^{14}\,Hz$

(e) Same as (d) – can calculate, but always same, frequency does not change
$3.3\times10^{14}\,Hz$

Example T4.7

$\dfrac{3\times10^{8}}{2.07\times10^{8}} = \dfrac{\sin 60}{\sin\theta_2} \Rightarrow \theta_2 = 36.69°$

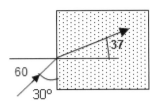

Example T4.8

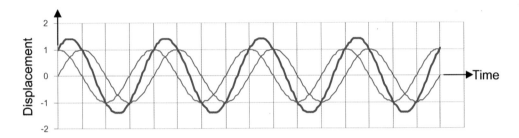

Topic 5: Electric Circuits

Example T5.1

$\Delta V = \dfrac{W}{q} = \dfrac{1.08\times10^{-17}}{1.6\times10^{-19}} = 67.5V$

Example T5.2

$W = \Delta V q = 500\times1.6\times10^{-19} = 8\times10^{-17}\,J$

Example T5.3

$R = \dfrac{\rho L}{A} = 1.09\,m\Omega \quad (A = 2\pi r)$

Example T5.4

a) $V = IR \Rightarrow I = V/R = 12/30 = 0.4\,A$
b) $P = VI = 12\times0.4 = 4.8W$

Example T5.5

The voltage drop is often called "lost voltage" and is due to the internal resistance of the supply. The emf of the supply is 8 volts. 0.32V is "lost" across the internal resistance (inside the source), leaving 7.68V available for the extrenal resistor. The resistance of the internal resistance is $0.5\,\Omega$
($R = V/I = 0.32/0.64 = 0.5\Omega$)

Example T5.6

	5Ω	10Ω (a)	10Ω (b)	Total circuit
Voltage	5V	5V	15V	20V
Current	1.0A	0.5A	1.5A	1.5A
Resistance	5Ω	10Ω	10Ω	13.33Ω
Power	5W	2.5W	22.5W	30W
Charge passed in 1 sec	1.0C	0.5C	1.5C	1.5C

Example T5.7

(a) We can find the circuit current, using V=IR, and the fact that the current flowing through the external resistor is the total current.

$$V = IR \Rightarrow I = \frac{V}{R} = \frac{10V}{100\Omega} = 0.1A$$

(b) Again, using $V = IR = 0.1A \times 10\Omega = 1V$

(c) To solve internal resistance problems, it is a good idea to think of the internal resistor as no more than an additional external resistor – in series with the rest of the circuit. So the question is really asking if one resistor has a pd across it of 1V, and the other 10V, what is the pd across the supply?   Answer: 11V

(d) We have assumed that the voltmeter has an infinite resistance, so that it does not affect the circuit that it is in.

(e) To solve this, just treat the voltmeter as though it were an ordinary resistor and find the pd across it.

Think of the circuit as follows:

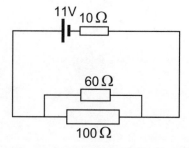

Question to be answered:

what is the pd across the 60 Ω resistor? (ie the voltmeter)

Total resistance: parallel resistors: $\dfrac{1}{R_T} = \dfrac{1}{60} + \dfrac{1}{100} = \dfrac{2}{75} \Rightarrow R_T = \dfrac{75}{2} = 37.5$

Therefore total resistance = $37.5\Omega + 10\Omega = 47.5\Omega$

Total current: $V = IR \Rightarrow I = \dfrac{V}{R} = \dfrac{11V}{47.5\Omega} = 0.232A$

pd across 10Ω resistor : $V = IR = 0.232A \times 10\Omega = 2.32V$

therefore, pd across the 60Ω (and 100Ω) resistor

= 11V – 2.32V   = 8.68V

Topic 6: Fields and Forces

Example T6.1

(a) Gravitational field: $g = \dfrac{F}{m} = \dfrac{98}{10} = 9.8 Nkg^{-1}$

(b) Electric field: $E = \dfrac{F}{q} = \dfrac{4.8 \times 10^{-17} N}{1.6 \times 10^{-19} C} = 300 NC^{-1}$

(c) Magnetic field: $B = \dfrac{F}{IL} = \dfrac{24 \times 10^{-3}}{1.25 \times 0.3} 0.064 T$

Example T6.2

(a)

$F_1 = F_2 = G \dfrac{m_1 m_2}{r^2} = 0.013 N$

(b)

$F_1 = F_2 = k \dfrac{q_1 q_2}{r^2} = 3.2 \times 10^{-4} N$

Example T6.3

(a) $E = k \dfrac{q}{r^2} = 1.4 mNC^{-1}$

(b) $g = G \dfrac{M}{r^2} = 3.3 \times 10^{-7} Nkg^{-1}$

Example T6.4

(a)

Combined field strength at midpoint (E_M) is due to contributions from proton (p) and electron (e) – and both act to the left

$E_M = E_p + E_e = k \dfrac{q_p}{r^2} + k \dfrac{q_e}{r^2} = 4.6 \times 10^{-4} NC^{-1}$

(b) Field strength is zero – both masses pull equally and in opposite directions.

(c)

$E_e = k \dfrac{q}{r^2} = 3.6 \times 10^{-4} NC^{-1}$

$E_p = k \dfrac{q}{r^2} = 3.6 \times 10^{-4} NC^{-1}$

$E_T = \sqrt{E_p^2 + E_e^2} = 5.1 \times 10^{-4} NC^{-1}$

Example T6.5

The wire and magnet both lie in the plane of the paper. Aligning the first finger pointing directly away from the north end of the magnet (which is the direction of the field) and aligning the second finger pointing down the page (which is the direction of the current), the thumb points directly out of the page. This is the direction of the force on the wire – and the direction of motion that would result.

Answer: The direction of the force is out of the page

Example T6.6

Example T6.7

The direction of the force can be found using Fleming's left hand rule: directly into the page

For the size:

$$B = \frac{F}{IL} \Rightarrow F = BIL$$

$$= 0.25T \times 0.8A \times 0.4m = 0.08N$$

Topic 7: Atomic and Nuclear Physics

Example T7.1

(a) The two nuclide are U-237 and U-238
(b) The nuclide with the greatest atomic mass is U-238. It has an atomic mass of 238, nucleon number of 238 and it has 92 protons and 146 neutrons in its nucleus.

Example T7.2

6 minutes goes into half an hour 5 times. ie. 5 half lives pass by. After each half life, one half of the radioactive material remains:

$1 \times \frac{1}{2} = \frac{1}{2}$ $\frac{1}{2} \times \frac{1}{2} = \frac{1}{4}$ etc.

So, after half an hour (30 minutes) $\frac{1}{32}$ of the sample remains

Therefore $\frac{31}{32}$ ($\approx 97\%$) of the sample has decayed.

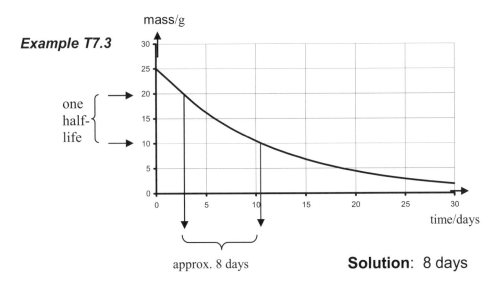

Example T7.3

approx. 8 days   **Solution**: 8 days

Example T7.4

$c = 4$, $d = 2$ since an α-particle has mass number, 4 and atomic number, 2

$e = 0$, $f = 0$ since a gamma ray is massless

$a = c + 206 + e = 4 + 206 + 0 = 210$ $b = d + 82 + f = 2 + 82 + 0 = 84$

so, $a = 210$, $b = 84$, $c = 4$, $d = 2$, $e = 0$, $f = 0$

Example T7.5

a) $^{238}_{92}U \rightarrow {}^{234}_{90}Th + {}^{4}_{2}\alpha$

b) $^{14}_{6}C \rightarrow {}^{14}_{7}N + {}^{0}_{-1}\beta \ (+\bar{\nu})$

c) $^{60}_{27}Co \rightarrow {}^{60}_{28}Ni^{*} + {}^{0}_{-1}\beta \ (+\bar{\nu})$

$\downarrow$

$^{60}_{28}Ni + \gamma$

Example T7.6

$E = mc^2 = 1.00 \times 10^{-3} \times (3.00 \times 10^8)^2 = 9.00 \times 10^{13}$

Answer : $9.00 \times 10^{13} J$

Example T7.7

A helium atom has 2 electrons, 2 protons and 2 neutrons

$mass\,defect = (2 \times 0.000549u + 2 \times 1.007276u + 2 \times 1.008665u) - 4.00260u$

$= 0.03038u$

$= 0.03038 \times 1.661 \times 10^{-27} \, kg$

$= 5.046 \times 10^{-29} \, kg$

$binding\ energy, E = mc^2 = 5.046 \times 10^{-29}(3.00 \times 10^8)^2$

$= 4.54 \times 10^{-12} J$

Example T7.8

Pb-206 is the most stable nuclide because according to the graph it has the highest binding energy per nucleon. If Po-210 undergoes a fission reaction to produce a lighter, more stable nuclide (Pb-206), energy will therefore be released.

Mass of reactants (left hand side) $= 209.983u$

Mass of products $= (205.974u + 4.003u) = 209.977u$

$\therefore$ Mass difference $= 0.006u$

$E = mc^2 = 0.006 \times 1.661 \times 10^{-27} \times (3.00 \times 10^8)^2 = 8.969 \times 10^{-13}$

Answer : $8.969 \times 10^{-13} J$

This may not seem like much energy, but it equates to over 2,500 megajoules of energy per gram of polonium!!

Topic 8: Energy, Power and Climate Change

Example T8.1

$$energy\ density = \frac{energy}{mass} \Rightarrow mass = \frac{energy}{energy\ density}$$

$$energy = power \times time = 400 \times 10^6 \times 24 \times 60 \times 60 = 3.5 \times 10^{13} J$$

$$\therefore mass = \frac{3.5 \times 10^{13}}{energy\ density}$$

Natural gas: 690 thousand kg
Crude oil: 768 thousand kg
Coal: 1.4 million kg
Water: 35 thousand million kg
U-235: 390g

Example T8.2

(a) $P = IA = 1400 \times 4\pi(150 \times 10^9)^2 = 4.0 \times 10^{26} W$

(b) $I = \dfrac{P}{A} = \dfrac{4.0 \times 10^{26}}{4\pi(780 \times 10^9)^2} = 52 Wm^{-1}$

Example T8.3

$$P_{(sun)} = 0.95 \times 5.67 \times 10^{-8} \times 4\pi(7 \times 10^8)^2 \times 5800^4 = 3.8 \times 10^{26} W$$

$$P_{(Earth)} = 0.7 \times 5.67 \times 10^{-8} \times 4\pi(6.4 \times 10^6)^2 \times (273 + 25)^4 = 1.6 \times 10^{17} W$$

Example T8.4

$$300Wm^{-2} = 300Jm^{-2} \ per \ second$$

$$\therefore \frac{Q}{A} \ (energy \ per \ m^{-2}) = 300 \times 60 \times 60 \times 24 \times 3 \times 7$$

$$= 5.44 \times 10^8 \, Jm^{-2} \ (in \ 3 \ weeks)$$

$$C_s = \frac{Q}{A\Delta T} = \frac{5.44 \times 10^8}{2} = 2.7 \, Jm^{-2} K^{-1}$$

Note that in this example we did not need the surface area of the lake.
(We would need this if we were told only the total energy absorbed by the lake, rather than the energy intensity, as in the above example)

Topic Nine: Motion in Fields

Review of Gravitational Fields and Introduction to Projectiles

Projectile motion is motion under the influence of a uniform field.
In this course we study projectile motion in a uniform gravitational field.
A uniform field is one which is the same size everywhere and is always in the same direction.

We assume a uniform gravitational field at and around the surface of the Earth.

Gravitational field lines are the lines followed by a test mass placed in the field.
At the surface of the Earth, the field lines are considered to be parallel and point towards the Earth, at 90° to the flat, horizontal surface. This is consistent with a uniform field.

Gravitational Field strength is defined to be the force per unit mass acting on a test mass when placed in the field.

(A test mass is one small enough not to affect the shape of the field it is in)

Hence: $g = \dfrac{F}{m}$

g, often known simply as "gravity" is better termed "gravitational field strength".

g at the surface of the Earth is known to be $9.81\, Nkg^{-1}$
(It can be shown that g also measures acceleration due to gravity and thus can also have units of acceleration – hence, we also know g as $9.81\, ms^{-2}$)

Do not confuse the constant, $g = 9.81\, Nkg^{-1} = 9.81\, ms^{-2}$, the gravitational field strength or acceleration due to gravity **at the surface of the Earth**, with the general quantity g, which measures the general gravitational field strength for any position in the proximity of any mass.

Hence, if the Earth is treated as a planet of finite size in an infinitely larger universe, the field strength is in fact variable and decreases as one moves away from the planet. Field lines are no longer considered parallel, but radial and non-uniform, pointing towards the centre of the Earth.

We have learned (Topic 6) how to find this value (field strength) at any position.

On the surface of the Earth, masses experience $g = 9.81\, Nkg^{-1}$, and so this is the field strength.

The force due to gravity, using the above equation, is $F = mg$.

This force is also given the name weight (and often loosely called "gravity"). Hence the equation "weight = mass x gravity" – weight is the force, "gravity", here, is gravitational field strength.

Projectile Motion.

A projectile is a mass moving through a uniform (gravitational) field.
This type of motion only commences once the mass has departed from the contact force causing its projection.
The path taken by a projectile is called a trajectory.

It can be shown that all trajectories are parabolic in shape (except when the projectile is thrown vertically upwards or downwards).

The essence of projectile motion is that, regardless of the direction and speed of a projectile, the force acting on it is constant (since the mass is constant and the field strength is constant) and $F = mg$.

So any object "flying through the air" only has one force acting on it: its weight, acting vertically downwards.

This, of course, assumes zero air resistance, which is not completely accurate but serves as a means for quite accurate velocity and displacement calculations provided that the mass is fairly dense and therefore air resistance forces are small compared with its weight.

To solve projectile problems we use the following method –we split the motion into horizontal and vertical motion and we take horizontal motion to be at uniform speed and vertical motion to be at uniform acceleration. Thus:

For horizontal motion the only equation we can use is: $speed = \dfrac{distance}{time}$

For vertical motion we use the equations of motion and (assuming we are on the surface of the Earth) that acceleration, g is equal to $9.81\ ms^{-2}$

The time for the horizontal motion is always the same as the time for the vertical motion for any trajectory.

Example T9.1

A ball is projected horizontally from a point 5.0 metres above the ground at a speed of $8.0ms^{-1}$ What is the range of the ball and what is its speed as it makes initial impact with the ground. State any assumptions.

Example T9.2

What is the optimum angle from the horizontal in order to maximize the range of a projectile, assuming negligible air resistance?

Example T9.3

An experiment is carried out, projecting a ball from one building to another. The angle of projection and speed of projection can be varied. The following diagram illustrates the situation:

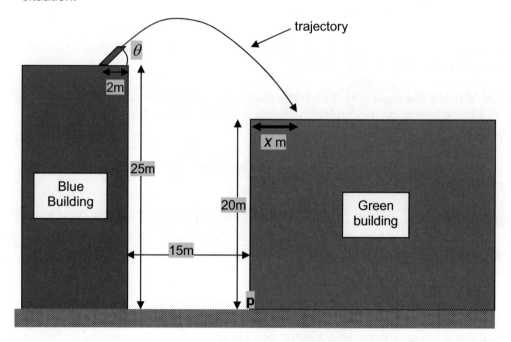

The ball is projected 2m from the edge of the blue building, at an angle θ from the horizontal. Assume that the green building is very wide and that the height from which the ball is projected is at the top of the blue building (the projector is not raised above the roof of the blue building)

(a) If the ball is projected at 40° to the horizontal, at a speed of $12ms^{-1}$:
       i) find the maximum height above the ground reached by the ball
       ii) find the value of x , giving the position where it hits the green building
       iii) find the speed at which it hits the building

(b) At the same angle (40°), find the speed that the ball should be projected in order for it to land just at the base of the green building, labelled **P** on the diagram

Gravitational and Electric Field, Potential and Energy

Gravitational fields and Electric fields are almost identical, in concept and in mathematical treatment.

To illustrate this, and to help you to be able to draw comparisons, I shall deal with them simultaneously.

Gravitational Potential Energy

The GPE is a quantity associated with a mass at a certain position in a gravitational field.

Hence, a mass in a gravitational field will have a potential energy due to its presence in the field.

Definition: The GPE of a mass is the energy required (work done) to move it from infinity (ie outside the field) to its position in the field.

Since gravitational fields are always attractive, work will not be required to move masses into the field – in fact, energy is liberated (work is done to move them out of the field).

Hence, the gravitational potential energy of a mass in a field is always negative. The maximum GPE a mass can have is zero – and this is when it has escaped the field.

The average human being (mass 65kg) has a gravitational potential of approximately -4000 *million joules*

Electric Potential Energy

Electric Potential energy is the energy of a charge due to its position (in an electric field).

Definition: The electric potential energy (of a charge) is the work done (or energy required) to bring the charge in question from infinity (ie from outside the field) to the point in question.

For example a proton placed next to a positive charge would require work to be done to get it there, so it has positive potential energy. However, an electron placed at the same position would have actually accelerated there (if allowed to), and so would have released energy (rather than having to be worked on) so the electron would have a negative potential energy.

Like masses, charges at infinite distance have zero potential energy.

Comparison: charges in an attractive field have negative potential energies, in a similar way to masses in gravitational fields (always attractive).

Gravitational Potential

Gravitational Potential is a quantity associated with a position in a gravitational field.

It allows us to calculate the GPE of a mass at that position.

Definition: Gravitational Potential (of a position) is the work done per unit mass in bringing a test mass from infinity to that position in the field.

So gravitational potential is simply GPE per kilogram.

Note, though, that the quantity measures the field position rather than any measurement of a mass.

To convert potential into potential energy:

$$E_p = mV_g \text{ (not given in data booklet)}$$

i.e. Gravitational Potential Energy = mass x gravitational potential.

Note that the IB data booklet simply uses the symbol V (not V_g) for gravitational potential – which is a little confusing!

The surface of the Earth has a gravitational potential of around $-63\ MJkg^{-1}$

We can calculate gravitational potential (and hence GPE) as follows:

$$V = -\frac{Gm}{r}$$

G is the universal constant of gravitation

m is the mass

V is the (grav.) potential, distance r from the centre of the mass

To find the **potential energy** of another mass at this position, just multiply the above expression by the other mass.

(Note that $\Delta E_p = mg\Delta h$ only applies when *g* is constant)

Note also: $\quad \Delta V = \frac{\Delta E_p}{m}$

Finally note that work done = change in potential energy (ie there will be a corresponding energy change elsewhere if we have a change in GPE)

Example T9.4

Universal constant of gravitation (G) $= 6.67 \times 10^{-11}\ Nm^2 kg^{-2}$

Mass of Earth $\qquad\qquad\qquad = 6.0 \times 10^{24}\ kg$

Radius of Earth $\qquad\qquad\quad = 6380\ km$

(i) Calculate the gravitational potential:

        (a) at the surface of the earth
        (b) 50 km above the surface of the earth
        (c) 5000 km above the surface of the earth

(ii) Using (i) calculate the gravitational potential energy of a 50kg mass

        (a) at the surface,
        (b) 50 km above the surface
        (c) 5000 km above the surface

(iii) Using (ii) (and by calculating the GPE change) Calculate the work done in moving a 50kg mass from the surface of the earth to:

        (a) 50 km above the surface of the earth (b) 5000 km above the surface of the earth

(iv) Use the equation $\Delta E_p = mg\Delta h$ to re-solve the questions in (iii). Compare answers using these two methods and comment.

Notes:

- the work done in moving a mass between two points in a gravitational field is independent of the path taken – so it is the same as long as you start at the same place and finish at the same place.

- gravitational field strength is a vector quantity

- gravitational potential (and potential energy) is a scalar quantity

Electric Potential

Electric Potential is a quantity associated with a position in an electric field.

It allows us to calculate the EPE (electric potential energy) of a charge at that position.

Definition: Electric Potential (of a position) is the work done, per unit charge, in bringing a positive test charge from infinity to that position in the field.

So electric potential is simply EPE per coulomb.

Note, though, that the quantity measures the field **position** rather than any measurement of a charge.

Note also that, purely by convention, to define electric potential we imagine that we are moving a **positive** test charge from infinity to the point.

To convert potential into potential energy:

$$E_p = qV_E \text{ (not given in data book)}$$

i.e. Electric Potential Energy = charge x electric potential.

Note that the IB data booklet simply uses the symbol V (not V_E) for electric potential

We can calculate electric potential (and hence EPE) as follows:

$$V = \frac{kq}{r}$$

k is the coulomb constant

q is the charge

V is the (elect.) potential, distance r from the centre of the charge

To find the **potential energy** of another charge at this position, just multiply the above expression by the charge.

Note: $\Delta V = \frac{\Delta E_p}{q}$ where ΔV is the potential difference (voltage)

Finally note that work done = change in potential energy (ie there will be a corresponding energy change elsewhere if we have a change in EPE)

Example T9.5

Coulomb constant (k)	$= 8.99 \times 10^9 \ Nm^2C^{-2}$
Charge of an electron	$= -1.6 \times 10^{-19} C$
Charge of a proton	$= 1.6 \times 10^{-19} C$

(i) Calculate the electric potential:

        (a) 1.0mm from an electron
        (b) 1.0mm from a proton
        (c) at the surface of an alpha particle (charge 2+), of radius $1.4 \ fm$

(ii) Using (i), where possible, calculate the electric potential energy of:

        (a) a proton 1.0mm from an electron,
        (b) a proton 1.0mm from a proton
        (c) an electron $10^{-12} \ m$ from the centre of an alpha particle

(iii) Calculate the work done by an electron when it moves from a position 1 mm from an isolated electron to another position 3mm from an isolated proton

Notes:

- the work done in moving a charge between two points in an electric field is independent of the path taken – so it is the same as long as you start at the same place and finish at the same place.

- electric field strength is a vector quantity

- electric potential (and potential energy) is a scalar quantity

Hopefully, you can see that the mathematical treatment for potential and potential energy is almost identical for charges and for masses – except that for charges, you can have positive of negative values, whereas with masses the values can only be negative.

<u>**Further examples:**</u>

Example T9.6

        (a) Find the potential energy difference of a +2.00nC charge moving between two plates with voltage across them (potential difference) of 400V
        (b) assuming that the charge has a mass of 4.15 x 10^{-15} kg, and that it is placed at the positive plate, find the speed when it reaches the negative plate

Example T9.7

The potential energy difference between an electron at point A and electron at point B is 1.08 x 10^{-17} J. Find the potential difference between the points.

Potential Gradient and Equipotentials.

Potential Gradient

This quantity measures how quickly potential changes, with distance.

Definition: Potential gradient is the rate of change of potential with distance between two points in a (gravitational / electric) field.

Gravitational potential gradient is given the symbol: $\frac{\Delta V}{\Delta r}$ in the IB data booklet.

Equipotentials

Points at the same distance above the Earth's surface are all at the same (gravitational) potential – such surfaces are called equipotentials, or equipotential surfaces.

So the potential gradient along points placed "horizontally" is zero.

However, vertically, potential changes.

Since the energy of a 1 kg mass increases by 9.81 joules per metre (using $E = mg\Delta h$), we can say that the potential above the Earth's surface increases by $9.81\,Jkg^{-1}$ per metre, and, therefore, the potential gradient above the Earth's surface is $9.81\,Jkg^{-1}m^{-1}$

Example T9.8

By finding the gravitational potential at the Earth's surface and at 1m above the Earth's surface, find the (gravitational) potential gradient around the surface of the Earth.

Example T9.9

Find the electric potential gradient between a $+100V$ charged plate and a $-100V$ charged plate that are parallel and placed 1.5mm apart

Relationship between field strength and potential gradient

We can see in the above example (T9.9) that the potential gradient is equal in magnitude (size) to field strength. It can be shown that this is always true. Hence:

$g = -\frac{\Delta V}{\Delta r}$ in words, gravitational field strength is equal (in magnitude) to potential gradient (the negative sign indicates that the direction of the field is opposite to the direction of increasing potential)

And, for electric fields:

$E = -\frac{\Delta V}{\Delta r}$ in words, electric field strength is equal (in magnitude) to potential gradient (the negative sign indicates that the direction of the field is opposite to the direction of increasing potential)

Another relationship between fields and potential is that equipotentials are always at right angles (perpendicular) to field lines.

We can use this fact to plot equipotentials by ensuring that they are always perpendicular to field lines.

Example T9.10

For the following two-planet system, show the field lines (using lines with arrows) and the equipotential surfaces:

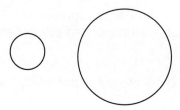

Calculation of the potential due to two or more masses (or charges)

Example T9.11

Given that the moon has a mass of $7.36 \times 10^{22} kg$ ($Earth: 6.0 \times 10^{24} kg$) and the distance between centres of moon and Earth is $384000 km$, find the gravitational potential midway between the centres of the moon and earth.

Strictly, when we calculate the potential at the surface of the earth, we should take into account the potential due to the presence of the moon – but the moon's presence would have an insignificant effect due to it being so far away.

Example T9.12

Calculate the electric potential midway between:

    (i)   two electrons placed 1mm apart
    (ii)   an electron and a proton placed 1mm apart

Example T9.13

Draw the field lines (in blue) and equipotential surfaces (in red) for the following charged surfaces

(i) A positively charged sphere   (ii) Two parallel plates

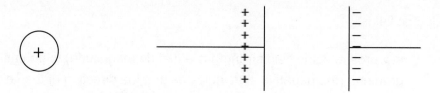

Escape Speed

In order for a mass to escape from a planet, it must be given enough energy for it to be able to increase its gravitational potential energy to zero.

There is thus an energy change: the energy it possesses is converted into gravitational energy: it moves 'upwards" away from the planet.

This energy source could be, for example, chemical energy. For instance, a rocket burns fuel to produce thrust to power it upwards. The associated energy conversion is from chemical energy to gravitational potential energy (note that if it is not actually getting faster, there is no continual transfer to kinetic energy).

An alternative way to give an object enough energy to escape is to give it kinetic energy. The speed associated with this kinetic energy – the energy required for it to escape the planet – is called the escape velocity, or escape speed.

Derivation of escape speed formula:

Energy required to escape = change in GPE

Final necessary potential = zero

Initial potential = $V = -\dfrac{GM}{r}$ where M is the mass of the planet and r,the distance from the planet = planet radius.

Change in potential = $\Delta V = final - initial = 0 - -\dfrac{GM}{r} = +\dfrac{GM}{r}$

Change in potential energy, $\Delta E_P = m\Delta V$ where m is the mass of the object escaping

$$\therefore \Delta E_P = m\frac{GM}{r}$$

If we provide the object with this amount of energy as kinetic energy, its kinetic energy will therefore equate to the above energy. Hence:

kinetic energy = $m\dfrac{GM}{r}$

$$\therefore \frac{1}{2}mv^2 = m\frac{GM}{r} \implies v^2 = 2\frac{GM}{r} \implies v = \sqrt{\frac{2GM}{r}}$$

$v_{esc} = \sqrt{\dfrac{2GM}{r}}$ where v_{esc} is the velocity required for a mass to escape from a planet of mass M and radius r

(formula not given in data booklet!)

Note that escape speed is independent of the size of the object escaping from the planet.

Example T9.14

Find the theoretical escape speed of a mass:

  (i)   on the moon
  (ii) on Earth

> Radius of Earth = $6380\ km$
> Radius of Moon = $1740\ km$
> Mass of Earth = $6.0 \times 10^{24}\ kg$
> Mass of Moon = $7.4 \times 10^{22}\ kg$
> G = $6.67 \times 10^{-11}\ Nm^2kg^{-2}$

Orbital Motion

An orbit is the path followed by an object around another object, or around a point. For example the moon is said to orbit the Earth.
We only consider circular orbits.

Objects moving in circles at constant speed are continually accelerating, because they are continually changing direction and therefore velocity. It can be shown that this acceleration is always directed towards the centre of the circle. This acceleration is called centripetal acceleration. There is therefore a resultant force required to keep a mass moving in a circle. This force is called centripetal force. This force can come from a variety of sources. For example, it can be the tension in a piece of string (with a mass on the end, twirling in a circle).

In the case of planets or satellites (such as moons – natural satellites) centripetal force is provided by the gravitational attraction between the planet and star (for planets orbiting stars), or between planets and satellites (for satellites orbiting planets).

Kepler's Third Law:

This law describes the relationship between the time taken for a planet to orbit the sun and its average (mean) distance from the sun. As the distance (orbit radius) increases it is not surprising that the orbit time also increases but the exact relationship is not immediately obvious.

The law states that the square of the time of revolution of a planet (ie its period time, T) is proportional to the cube of the mean distance (r) from it.

$$\text{ie: } r^3 \propto T^2 \text{ or } \frac{r^3}{T^2} = \text{a constant}$$

Example T9.15

If planet A has an average orbit radius twice that of B, by what factor is its orbit time period greater than that of planet B?

Example T9.16

Given that Earth has an orbit time period about the sun of 1 year (3.16×10^7 seconds) and that Uranus has an orbit time period of 84.0 years, and that the mean distance from the Earth to the sun is 1.49×10^{11} metres, calculate an expected mean orbit radius for Uranus, and state this as a ratio to that for Earth.

Kepler's Third Law – derivation

An orbiting satellite can be assumed to be moving in an approximate circle. It therefore requires a force, called centripetal force, to maintain its path. The force is provided by the gravitational attraction between the satellite and the planet that it is orbiting. So centripetal force required = gravitational force provided. (If gravitational force is larger than centripetal force required, satellite would spiral into the planet, if is it smaller, satellite would spiral outwards into space).

Algebraically:

gravitational force $=$ centripetal force

$$\Rightarrow \frac{GMm}{r^2} = \frac{mv^2}{r} \Rightarrow v^2 = \frac{GM}{r}$$

(where m is mass of satellite; M is mass of planet, r is distance between centres)

but, since speed is constant, $v = \dfrac{\text{distance}}{\text{time}} = \dfrac{2\pi r}{T}$

(if we take distance as one complete orbit, radius r, $T =$ time period)

$$\left(\frac{2\pi r}{T}\right)^2 = \frac{GM}{r} \Rightarrow \frac{4\pi^2 r^2}{T^2} = \frac{GM}{r} \Rightarrow \frac{r^3}{T^2} = \frac{GM}{4\pi^2} \approx 1.01 \times 10^{13}\ (\text{a constant})$$

Therefore $\dfrac{r^3}{T^2} = \text{constant}$

An interesting consequence of Kepler's third Law is the fact that geostationary satellites have to all be the same distance above the Earth. Since $r^3 \propto T^2$, it follows that at a certain distance from the Earth, a satellite will have a certain time period (orbit time). A geostationary satellite has to follow a point on the Earth, so it has to have a time period the same as the time taken for a single rotation of the Earth about its axis – ie. 1 day. Therefore we can easily calculate such a satellite's distance above the Earth.

Example T9.17

Calculate the orbit height of an Earth geostationary satellite.

Satellite Energy

A satellite will have gravitational potential energy due to its position in a gravitational field, and kinetic energy due to its movement. Once it is in place, orbiting the planet, its total energy will remain constant – there is no resistance, since it will be out of the planet's atmosphere. It is therefore easy to deduce that if the orbit is not perfectly circular, then as it moves closer to the planet, its potential energy will decrease and therefore its kinetic energy will increase. As a satellite moves closer to a planet its speed therefore increases.

Satellite Energies – derivation

$E_k = \frac{1}{2}mv^2$, where m is mass of satellite and v, speed

but $\dfrac{mv^2}{r} = \dfrac{GMm}{r^2}$ (equating centripetal and gravitational forces, as earlier)

where M is mass of planet being orbited

$$\Rightarrow mv^2 = \frac{rGMm}{r^2} = \frac{GMm}{r} \Rightarrow \tfrac{1}{2}mv^2 = \tfrac{1}{2}\frac{GMm}{r} = \frac{GMm}{2r}$$

So, $E_k = \dfrac{GMm}{2r}$ (kinetic energy)

We already have that $E_p = -\dfrac{GMm}{r}$ so, $E_T = \dfrac{GMm}{2r} + -\dfrac{GMm}{r} = -\dfrac{GMm}{2r}$

$$\text{Summary}: E_k = \frac{GMm}{2r},\ E_p = -\frac{GMm}{r},\ E_{Total} = -\frac{GMm}{2r}$$

The following graph shows how kinetic energy, (gravitational) potential energy and total energy for a satellite vary as its distance (number of planet radii) from a planet increases.

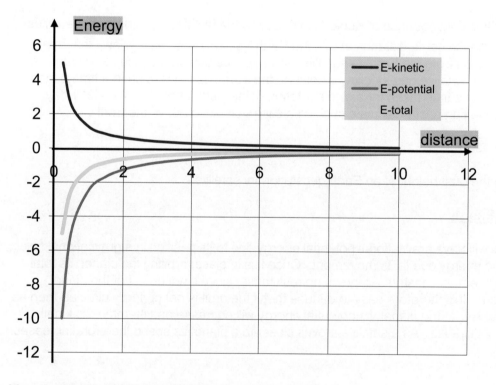

You need to be able to produce these sketch graphs.

Notes

- Potential energy is always negative – its maximum value is zero when it escapes the planet's field.

- Total energy is always negative – this is because kinetic energy is never great enough to overcome (negative) potential energy – if it were, the satellite would escape the planet, and fly off into space with zero potential (out of the field) and positive kinetic energy (moving). The graph refers only to satellites in orbit, so total energy must be negative.

Example T9.18

Calculate the kinetic energy, potential energy and total energy of a 650kg geostationary satellite. (Hint – use the distance from centre of Earth as calculated in Example T9.17)

Weightlessness

There are two kinds of weightlessness: true weightlessness, where an object has no weight, and apparent weightlessness.

True weightlessness can only be experienced by a mass when it is in a zero-gravitational field. This can happen in deep space or when the net field is zero – for example, at a certain point between the moon and Earth, where the attractive field from each cancel each other out.
More common and practically achievable, and with the same sensation, is apparent weightlessness. Apparent weightlessness is experienced by masses for which the only force acting on them is their weight. To help explain this concept, consider a man standing on the ground. He only feels his weight because of the contact force of the ground (normal reaction force) pushing up on him. The full weight of a mass is only experienced when resultant force is zero – ie when there is an opposing force equal to weight. A person jumping from an airplane experiences weightlessness to some extent – but air resistance prevents true weightlessness, except at the moment the person begins to fall, when air resistance is effectively zero.

We consider two examples of apparent weightlessness. The first situation is when a mass is falling and in a state of free fall as described above, with the only force being weight. The second situation is when a satellite is in orbit. Again, the only force acting is its weight. The motion of the satellite makes this concept difficult to understand. It moves in a circle, but it is always accelerating towards the centre of the circle, and its weight provides the force to do this. Its weight (ie. the gravitational force of attraction between the planet and the satellite) is the centripetal force required to allow it to maintain a circle.

Topic Ten: Thermal Physics

Thermodynamics

Ideal Gases

Definition: An ideal gas is one that obeys the equation of state. i.e.

$PV = nRT$ where $P = pressure\ of\ gas\ (Pa)$
$V = volume\ of\ gas\ (m^3)$
$n = number\ of\ moles\ of\ gas$
$R = molar\ gas\ constant\ (8.31\ JK^{-1}mol^{-1})$
$T = absolue\ temperature\ of\ gas\ (K)$

For a fixed mass of such a gas:

- pressure α temperature at constant volume (α means "is proportional to")
- volume α temperature at constant pressure
- pressure α $\dfrac{1}{volume}$ at constant temperature

(temperature is absolute (Kelvin) temperature in each case – see below)

Deviation from ideality

In general, most gases approximate closely to ideal gases. To behave as ideal gases:

- The particles themselves occupy zero volume
- There are no intermolecular forces between particles

Gases deviate from ideality under conditions of very high pressure (above critical pressure) and/or very low temperature (below *critical* temperature)

Note that ideal gases cannot be liquefied

Temperature Scales

The two common temperature scales are the Celsius temperature scale and the Kelvin temperature scale. The Kelvin scale is also referred as the absolute temperature scale. The absolute (Kelvin) temperature scale starts at the lowest possible temperature – zero Kelvin (0 K – degrees word and sign is omitted)). This equates to a temperature of –273 °C. Since an increment of 1°C is the same as an increment of 1 K, converting from °C to K or visa versa is very easy.

To convert from °C to K: Add   273
To convert from K to °C: Subtract   273

Examples:

0 K	=	$-273\,°C$
0 °C	=	$273\,K$
100 °C	=	$373\,K$
150 K	=	$-123\,°C$

Amount of Substance (moles)

Gas pressure does not depend on mass of particles, but rather, the number of particles of a given gas. For example 1000 molecules per cubic metre of hydrogen gas at room temperature will exert the same pressure as 1000 molecules per cubic metre of oxygen molecules – even though oxygen molecules are some 16 times more massive than hydrogen molecules.

The above example uses simple, but unrealistic numbers. At room temperature and pressure, one cubic metre will contain about 2.5×10^{25} molecules! We use a more convenient unit to measure "number of particles" – the mole.

One mole of particles is the same number of particles as there are atoms in 12g of carbon-12 (one of the isotopes of carbon)

This number is called the Avogadro constant, N_A, where
$N_A = 6.02 \times 10^{23}\,mol^{-1}$

Molar mass is the mass of one mole of a particular substance.

Example T10.1 (Using the equation of state of an ideal gas):

By assuming that air is made up of pure nitrogen gas, find an approximation of the mass of air in a container measuring 25cm x 50cm x 50cm at normal atmospheric pressure and room temperature. Use the following data:

normal atmospheric pressure	= 101 KPa
room temperature	= 25°C
gas constant, R	= 8.31JK^{-1} mol^{-1}
molar mass of nitrogen gas	= 28g

Thermodynamic Systems

A system is the entity being investigated or considered.
The surroundings is everything outside the system
A closed system is one for which no mass enters or leaves
An isolated system is one for which no energy enters or leaves

Heat, Work and Internal Energy

We consider these concepts in the context of an ideal gas. I shall summarise the key points as follows:

- The internal energy of an ideal gas is the total kinetic energy of the gas particles
- Internal energy can be increased by heating the gas or doing work on the gas.
- The gas is heated by exposing it to higher temperature surroundings. Heating is the process whereby energy flows from a hot object to a cooler object, due to this temperature difference.
- Work is done on the gas by applying a force on the gas and compressing the gas.

Work Done on a Gas – Derivation

Recall that the work done by a force = force x distance (in direction of the force)

Consider gas in a closed syringe. A force is applied in order to compress the gas to a smaller volume. The force applied has to be equal to the force due to the pressure of the gas – to "overcome" the pressure. If the change in volume is small, the pressure can be considered to be approximately constant.

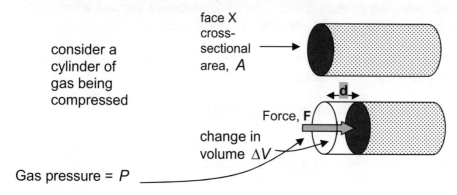

consider a cylinder of gas being compressed

face X cross-sectional area, A

Force, **F**

change in volume ΔV

Gas pressure = P

Gas exerts force on face X equal to $P \times A \left(P = \dfrac{F}{A} \Rightarrow F = PA \right)$

To compress gas, force needed = $P \times A$

Work done by force, on gas = force x distance = $P \times A \times d$

But, $A \times d = \Delta V$ (*volume change of gas*)

$\therefore$ *work done on gas* $= P\Delta V$, *written* $W = P\Delta V$

Note that in many practical situations the gas pressure increases as it is compressed.

(In these situations the work done on the gas can be found by finding the area under a graph of pressure versus volume.)

Example T10.2

A gas is reduced in volume by 2.5m^3 at normal atmospheric pressure (101 kPa). It then expands by 3.0 m^3. Find the work done on the gas during both stages, and the net work done on or by the gas.

If work done on gas is negative, as above, work is actually done by gas.

Hence,   if a gas expands, work is done **BY** the gas and its internal energy decreases as a result
If a gas is compressed (or contracts), work is done **ON** the gas and its internal energy increases as a result

The First Law of Thermodynamics

When thermal energy is added to a gas, either its internal energy is increased or the gas expands and does work.

The thermal energy transferred to a gas is equal to the increase in internal energy of the gas plus the work done by the gas. In symbols:

$Q = \Delta U + W$ where, Q = the thermal energy transferred to the system

ΔU = the increase in internal energy of the system

W = the work done BY the system (gas)

The first law is really a statement about the conservation of energy. Energy cannot be created or destroyed, only transferred to or from another source or place.

Example T10.3

Complete the following table, which refers to internal energy changes of an ideal gas at a constant pressure of 100kPa

	change in volume (m^3)	thermal energy transfer	work done	change in internal energy
i)	0.001 increase	1000J added		
ii)		1000J added	200J on gas	
iii)	.001 decrease	1000J added		
iv)		0J (insulated)	500J by gas	
v)	0 (const vol)			800J increase
vi)		600J removed		600J decrease
vii)		1000J removed		1000J increase

P-V diagrams and thermodynamic processes and cycles

As stated previously, the work done on or by a gas can be found by finding the area under a graph of pressure versus volume for the gas.

We shall now look at various types of thermodynamic processes.

Isobaric – at constant pressure

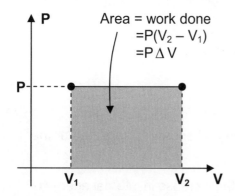

If volume starts at V_1 and ends at V_2, then work is done by the gas. If volume starts at V_2 and ends at V_1, work is done on the gas (work done by gas is negative). If gas expands from V_1 to V_2 and then contracts back to V_1, net work done is zero.

Isochoric – at constant volume

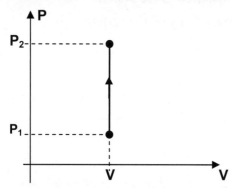

No work is done on or by the gas. (area under graph = zero) If pressure increases, temperature must also increase, so Q is positive in this case, and so is ΔU

Isothermal – at constant temperature

The equation of state (PV=nRT) tells us that at constant temperature PV is constant. Therefore $P \propto \dfrac{1}{V}$ The p-V diagram for pressure changes at constant temperature therefore looks like:

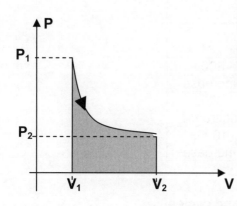

If the gas expands, as shown – from V_1 to V_2, then work is done by the gas. The work done by the gas can be found by finding the area under the curve, as indicated.

The above curve is known as an isotherm. Other isotherms occur at different temperatures, as follows.

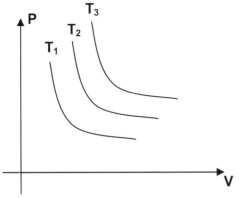

Each isotherm has to be precisely followed for a fixed mass of an ideal gas at that constant temperature. The curve moves to the right (upwards) if the temperature of the gas is higher. Hence $T_1 < T_2 < T_3$

For a gas undergoing an isothermal change:

$\Delta T = 0 \Rightarrow \Delta U = 0$, So, since $Q = \Delta U + W$, $Q = W$

i.e. the increase in thermal energy is equal to the work done by the gas.

The interpretation of this is that if thermal energy is added to the gas, since it it not allowed to increase in temperature, it expands. Conversely, if a gas is compressed, thermal energy must be transferred from the gas (and its temperature remains constant).

To achieve an isothermal change,

- the gas must not be insulated from its surroundings – thermal energy must be free to enter or leave the system
- the change (compression or expansion) should be performed slowly, to allow thermal energy to enter or leave the system rather than a change in temperature resulting
- the system should be immersed in a constant temperature water (or other fluid) bath so that a constant temperature is maintained

Adiabatic – no heat transfer allowed

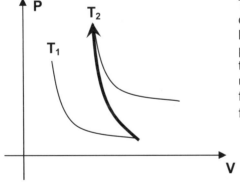

The path followed by an adiabatic compression is shown by the bold line. For such a compression, pressure increases and so does temperature. This can be explained using the equation of state and the first law of thermodynamics, as follows.

Since the process is adiabatic no heat transfer is allowed and $\Delta Q = 0$
Therefore, by the first law of thermodynamics: $\Delta U = \Delta W$
Assume that work is done on the gas (it is compressed) as shown on the diagram.
Then ΔU is positive – the internal energy of the gas increases. The internal energy of an ideal gas is a measurement of the average kinetic energy of its particles.

Hence the temperature of the gas must increase $(\Delta U = positive \Rightarrow \Delta T = positive)$. So far we have that volume decreases and temperature increases.

By the equation of state $\left(\dfrac{PV}{T} = \text{constant}\right)$ the pressure must increase (as indeed shown in diagram)

To ensure that an adiabatic process occurs thermal energy must not be allowed to enter or leave the system so it must be well insulated and the change (compression or expansion) should be carried out rapidly, minimizing any heat transfer to or from the system.

Thermodynamic cycles and work done

Depending on the conditions, any of the curves on the P-V diagrams shown may be followed. Processes are illustrated by adding arrows to the curves, showing the order and details of the changes. The work done during each change can be calculated using the area under the curve. Remember that work done BY a gas = –(work done ON a gas)

Example T10.4

The diagrams below show the processes followed by a gas. The blue lines show isothermals. In each case, describe the thermodynamic changes (numbered) taking place and shade the area representing the net work done on or by the gas in each case. Also state whether work is done on or by the gas.

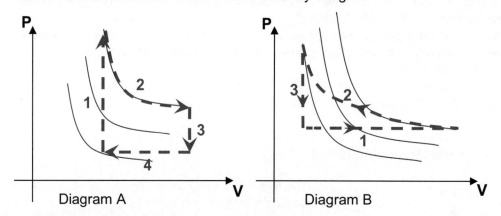

Diagram A   Diagram B

Example T10.5

The processed described in the table below refer to the changes of an ideal gas. Complete the table by inserting >0, <0 or =0 in each cell.

Process	Q	W	ΔU
Isobaric contraction			
Isothermal compression			
Adiabatic expansion			
Isochoric pressure drop			
Isothermal expansion			

Note
- If T changes, so does internal energy. (Internal energy $\propto$ T)
- $\dfrac{pV}{T} = \text{constant}$

Second Law of Thermodynamics

Entropy:

The entropy of a system is the state of disorder of that system.
Entropy increases if disorder increases.
State of disorder can be thought of state of randomness.

The second law of thermodynamics has been stated in different ways. Essentially, though, the law is a law about entropy, as follows:

"No process is possible in which there is an overall decrease in entropy of the universe"

Examples:

- Things get broken into many pieces (entropy increases), but do not mend themselves ("un-break") (entropy decreases) without some other process that increases entropy elsewhere. (overall entropy must not decrease)
- Energy concentrated in a gravitational potential energy store, due to a book on a shelf (low entropy) can be spread out amongst millions of particles in the air, as heat is released when it falls to the ground (higher entropy), but the reverse cannot happen simultaneously. (The book can be raised to the shelf, but by doing more work than is theoretically necessary there is a heat loss to surroundings– overall entropy increases)

Example T10.6

If a cup of cold water were to become hotter whilst the surroundings cooled down would this violate the law of conservation of energy or the second law of thermodynamics, or both?

Implication of second law

The spontaneous transfer of heat (energy) from a cold place to a hotter place is not possible. If it were possible, there would be a decrease in entropy in the universe, since the "cold place" is more ordered (in terms of particle arrangement) than the "hot place".

Topic 11: Wave Phenomena

Standing Waves

Standing waves are created by the interference of a wave and its reflection. Water waves, waves on strings and standing sound waves in open or closed tubes are some examples of standing waves that can easily be observed.

With water waves for example, waves approaching a harbour can combine with waves that have reflected off the harbour wall to result in large waves that are approximately stationary.

If a rope or rubber tube is waved up and down with one end fixed, a standing wave may be produced.

Standing waves are only formed at certain frequencies for certain strings (or pipes) at certain tensions.

Standing waves are an example of resonance.

Resonance can be achieved at more than one particular frequency.

The wave produced by the lowest resonant frequency is called the fundamental resonance, or the first harmonic.

The other resonances are called second, third, fourth etc. harmonics.

Standing Wave on String

The diagram shows a string being vibrated rapidly up and down from the left end. At the appropriate frequency (which depends on string length, tension and string mass per unit length) the string vibrates as the diagram shows, with zero-amplitude positions (nodes) at each end and the maximum amplitude position (antinode) half-way along the string.

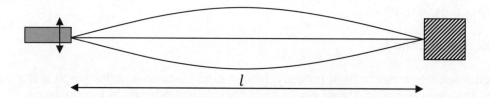

This is a side view of the string – note that at all points it is vibrating up and down – the three positions shown correspond to maximum positive and negative displacement and zero displacement. The diagram is a realistic picture of what is actually observed but if a snap-shot photograph is taken, the string would lie on a curve somewhere between these extremes – but only along one line (it is only one piece of string!)

Note that this wave section actually represents one-half of a complete wavelength. So, if the (horizontal) length of the string is l, $l = \frac{\lambda}{2}$ and so $\lambda = 2l$

If the vibration frequency is changed slightly, no particular pattern is observed, and the amplitude is significantly reduced (resonance is no longer being achieved). However, other positions of resonance are achievable at higher frequencies. All such standing waves are called harmonics.

We shall now consider simplified diagrams showing some of the harmonics produced by a wave on a string of length l and consider the wavelength of standing wave produced for each.

To construct these harmonics simply remember that there must be a node at each end of the string. For a string of length l (as shown on diagram):

i) Fundamental (First Harmonic)

$$l = \frac{\lambda}{2} \implies \lambda = 2l$$

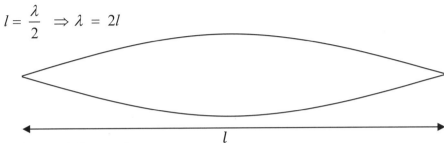

l

ii) Second Harmonic

$$\lambda = l$$

Example T11.1   Draw the third harmonic. Label nodes, antinodes and state the wavelength in terms of the string length

Notes
- The wavelength of the successive harmonics decrease in a pattern, such that $\lambda = \frac{2l}{n}$ where n is the number of the harmonic (e.g. for first harmonic, $n = 1$, so

$$\lambda = \frac{2l}{1} \implies \lambda = 2l$$

- Since the speed of the waves in the string (the waves moving along the string and interfering to form the standing wave) is constant for each set-up and string, the frequency is inversely proportional to the wavelength, (using the wave equation; $v = f\lambda$) so if, for example, the frequency of the first harmonic (fundamental) is f, then the second is $2f$, the third; $3f$ etc.

Standing Sound Wave in a Closed Pipe

If air is blown over an empty bottle at certain speeds, vibrations are set up inside the bottle and the resonant frequencies can be heard.

This is the situation with closed pipes: sound travels down the tube and reflects off the closed end, and back. At certain (resonant) frequencies standing waves are produced.

To construct these diagrams, just remember that there is always a node at the closed end and an antinode at the open end

For a closed pipe of length l

Fundamental (first harmonic)   next harmonic

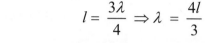

$$l = \frac{\lambda}{4} \Rightarrow \lambda = 4l \qquad\qquad l = \frac{3\lambda}{4} \Rightarrow \lambda = \frac{4l}{3}$$

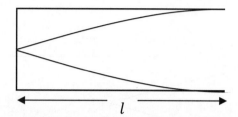   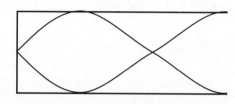

Note that the diagrams actually show how much the air particles are vibrating. At the open end of the tube, we can see that the air particles vibrate with maximum amplitude, and at the closed end, they are stationary. Note also that the air particles are actually vibrating, according to the diagram, left and right – since sound waves are reflected into and back out of the pipe. Sound waves are longitudinal and vibrate parallel to the direction in which the wave is trvelling.

Example T11.2 Draw the next harmonic and state expression for wavelength

Standing Sound Wave in an Open Pipe

Similarly, resonance and standing waves can be set up in an open pipe – waves, surprisingly, can reflect off the open end. The important difference here is that there are antinodes at both ends. Hence:

For an open ended pipe of length l

Fundamental   Second harmonic

$$l = \frac{\lambda}{2} \Rightarrow \lambda = 2l \qquad\qquad l = \lambda$$

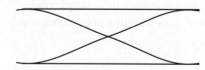   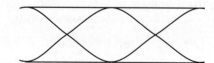

Example T11.3

Draw the **fourth** harmonic and state its wavelength in terms of the pipe length.

Notes:

For double open-ended pipes,

- General wavelength of n_{th} harmonic: $\lambda = \dfrac{2l}{n}$

In **all** standing wave situations,

- nodes are separated by a distance of $\dfrac{\lambda}{2}$ (this can be useful – e.g. in above

  example, there are 3 node-node spaces, making up $\dfrac{3\lambda}{2}$ wavelengths, add on

  two half node-node separations at the ends gives an extra $\dfrac{\lambda}{2}$. So total

  number of waves in the length shown is 2. Hence $l = 2\lambda \implies \lambda = \dfrac{l}{2}$

The Doppler Effect

When an ambulance speeds past a stationary observer, the note heard by the observer changes pitch. When approaching, the pitch is higher than usual and when moving away, the pitch is lower. This is an example of the Doppler Effect: when there is relative motion between a source of sound and an observer, the observed frequency is different from the emitted frequency. Hence a similar effect to that described above would be observed if an observer sped towards a stationary ambulance – the pitch would be greater as the observer approaches, and lower when departing.

To explain this, consider the wavefronts emitted from a sound source, marked ☼ and consider what the observers, marked 😊 and ☺ , will hear (Note that sound waves travel much faster than observers!):

Situation 1 – Observers and source stationary:

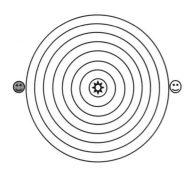

Wavefronts are all emitted from same point and thus form concentric circles with equally spaced circumferences

Both observers hear the sound at the same frequency as it is emitted

Situation 2: Source moving towards ☺ and away from 😊

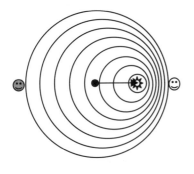

Source moves to right so center of each circular wavefront keeps moving to right
The effect is for wavefronts to bunch-up on the right and to spread apart on the left

Hence ☺ hears a higher than usual frequency and 😊 hears a lower than usual frequency.

Situation 3: Source stationary, both observers moving to right

(😎 towards ☀ and ☺ away from ☀)

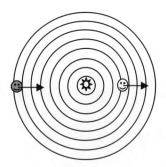

Observer 😎 moves towards the wavefronts so observes them more frequently

Observer ☺ moves away from the wavefronts (the ones on his right have already passed him) so observes them less frequently

Therefore the approaching observer hears sound of a higher frequency and the departing observer hears sound of a lower frequency

The Doppler effect is also observed with light (ie electromagnetic waves) – this is why stars moving away from an observer show a "red shift" and stars moving towards an observer show a "blue shift". (red light is the lowest frequency in the visible range and blue/violet, the highest).

Doppler Effect Equations for Sound

We have 4 equations: two for a moving source and two for a moving observer, as follows:

$$f' = f\left(\frac{v}{v \pm u_s}\right) \quad \textit{moving source}$$

$$(+ \textit{ for source moving away from observer}, - \textit{for towards})$$

$$f' = f\left(\frac{v \pm u_o}{v}\right) \quad \textit{moving observer}$$

$$(+ \textit{ for observer moving towards source}, - \textit{for away})$$

Where:

$f' = frequency\ of\ sound\ heard\ by\ observer$
$f = frequency\ of\ sound\ emitted\ by\ source$
$v = speed\ of\ sound\ (in\ air)$
$u_s = speed\ of\ source$
$u_o = speed\ of\ observer$

When using these equations, always check that your observed frequency has changed as expected.

Example T11.4

A car sounds its horn as it travels at a speed of $30ms^{-1}$ past Asaf and towards Buha, two people standing at the edge of a straight road. Describe, with calculations, the difference in the sound as observed by Asaf and by Buha. (The frequency of the sound emitted is 510Hz, and the speed of sound in air is 340ms⁻¹)

Doppler Equation for Electromagnetic Waves

$$\Delta f = \frac{v}{c} f$$ where $\Delta f = change\ in\ frequency\ (frequency\ shift)$
$v = relative\ velocity\ between\ source\ and\ observer$
$c = speed\ of\ light$
$f = frequency\ of\ electromagnetic\ wave\ (light) emitted$

The equation is an approximation that can only be used when v is much less than c

Example T11.5

A star emits light of wavelength 610nm. Light received at the Earth from this star is analysed as having a wavelength of 645nm. How fast is the star moving relative to the Earth and in what direction?

Examples of use of Doppler effect:

Blood flow rate – ultra-sound signals are directed into the body. The ultrasound machine can both emit and receive/detect the ultrasound signal. The machine can also measure the time delay and hence the depth of reflecting particle and can measure the frequency of the reflected signal. If the reflected signal has a higher frequency, then the reflecting particles must be moving towards the machine, and vice-versa for a lower frequency. The machine can thus calculate the speed of blood flow.

Police speed cameras also work on this principle but use microwaves or infrared radiation rather than ultrasound.

Diffraction

I described and explained diffraction in topic 4. We now consider diffraction at a single slit.

When light is directed towards a very narrow slit (like a single scratch on a painted glass slide) such that the width of the slit (this measurement is called b) is of the order of only a few wavelengths of the light, it emerges in a particular way, due to diffraction. If the light is projected onto a screen a diffraction pattern is observed.

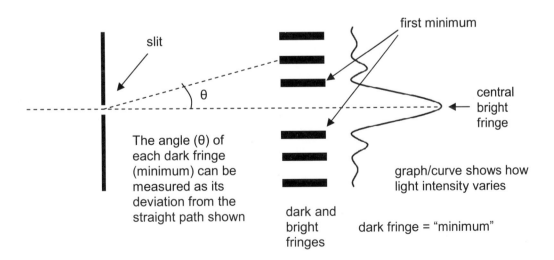

The light emerges in light and dark "fringes". The above diagram shows a simplified version of what is seen. The graph (usually see rotated 90° anti-clockwise) shows how the intensity varies with position. Thus, the central fringe has the greatest intensity and is the brightest.

It is possible to explain this pattern and to predict the positions of the dark fringes, as follows.

When a light-wave enters the slit, the wave is not a single ray, but a beam. Each crest that passes through the slit is called a wave-front. (The wave-fronts are at 90° to the beam).

Huygen's Principle tells us that we can consider a wave-front as a line of point sources of light. So effectively, when a wave-front enters the slit, we can think of this as an infinite number of light-rays.

These light rays can interact (interfere) with each other. At different positions along the screen there will be different types of interference.

In the centre a crest from one "point source" or ray will always be met by a crest from another, due to the symmetry. Similarly a trough from one wave at that point will be met by a trough from another. So in the centre constructive interference results. When two crests meet, a larger crest is formed; when two troughs meet, a larger trough is formed. The wave amplitude (and hence intensity) increases.

At a certain point a little way along from the centre, a crest from one wave will meet a trough from another, due to the slightly different distances the two waves have to travel and the asymmetry. Here there will be destructive interference and a dark fringe (minimum) will be observed.

The diagram overpage helps to explain this and allows us to derive a formula to predict the positions of each dark fringe.

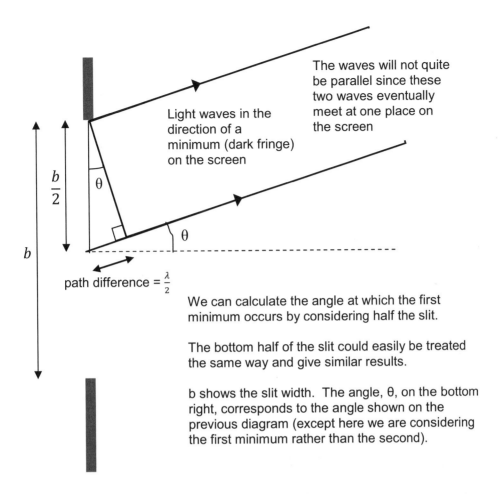

Light waves in the direction of a minimum (dark fringe) on the screen

The waves will not quite be parallel since these two waves eventually meet at one place on the screen

path difference $= \frac{\lambda}{2}$

We can calculate the angle at which the first minimum occurs by considering half the slit.

The bottom half of the slit could easily be treated the same way and give similar results.

b shows the slit width. The angle, θ, on the bottom right, corresponds to the angle shown on the previous diagram (except here we are considering the first minimum rather than the second).

Simple geometry tells us that the other angle shown on the diagram is the same; hence we can label it θ. An approximation here is that the two waves are indeed parallel – which is very close to true since the screen is so far away in comparison to the slit width.

For the first minimum to occur at the screen, one wave must meet the other exactly half a wavelength ahead. The path difference of the two waves must therefore be $\frac{\lambda}{2}$.

This path difference corresponds to the section of the triangle opposite θ shown in the diagram.

Using trigonometry, $\quad sin\theta = \frac{opp}{hyp} = \frac{\lambda/2}{b/2} = \frac{\lambda}{b} \quad$ Hence: $\lambda = bsin\theta$

If we work in radians, it can be shown that for very small angles (which we are dealing with here) $sin\theta \simeq \theta$. Hence we get: $\lambda = bsin\theta = b\theta$

So, for the first minimum: $\lambda = b\theta \implies \theta = \frac{\lambda}{b}$

For the second minimum we would get $\theta = \frac{3\lambda}{b}$ because to get this we would need a path difference of one and a half wavelengths.

We only need worry about the formula for the first minimum on this course.

Example T11.6

Light with a wavelength of 500nm is shone through a slit of width 0.04mm so that the diffraction pattern falls on a screen 4.5m away.
  (a) Calculate the position of the first minimum
  (b) Find the approximate width of the central bright fringe.

Resolution

Try drawing two small dots, very close together on a piece of paper.
As you move the paper away from your eyes the dots will, at a certain point, appear as a single dot.

If you see both dots you have successfully resolved the two dots. The ability to resolve decreases as the distance from the dots increases.

The reason you see the two dots as a single dot is that when light from each dot enter your eye the light diffracts as it passes through your pupil. This causes a diffraction pattern, for each dot, consisting of concentric circles (disks) as shown below. As the distance between your eye and the dots increase, the images (and diffraction patterns) begin to move together. When there is too much overlap the images are perceived as a single image (dot).

The diffraction pattern that will result when the human eye (or other circular aperture) views two dots.

Note that in this case (with the two patterns separated) the image will appear as two dots.

The Rayleigh Criterion

The Rayleigh criterion allows us to know if two points are resolvable (distinguishable as two separate points.

It states that **two points will be resolvable if the central maximum of the diffraction pattern formed of one point coincides with the first minimum of the other** (and this is the closest that the two diffractions can get to each other before they appear to be one point.

Thus, the following diagrams show diffraction patterns to illustrate resolved, just resolved and unresolved image:

(a) Resolved

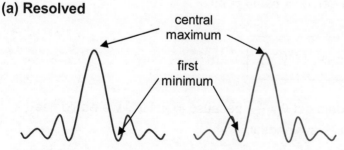

central maximum

first minimum

There is effectively no overlap between the two diffraction patterns
Blue and red patterns are shown here to aid the argument that follows.

The two diffractions can move together until they reach the limit prescribed by the Rayleigh Criterion. Hence:

(b) Just resolved

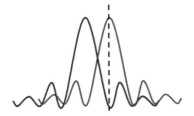

The central maximum from the red pattern has overlapped to the point that it overlaps the first minimum of the blue pattern

If the two patterns overlap any further they will be appear as a single image. Hence:

(c) Unresolved

The blue and red diffraction patterns now go beyond the level of overlap as prescribed by the Rayleigh Criterion: they lines will thus appear as a single line.

Applying the Rayleigh Criterion to human vision

For human vision, the aperture through which the light passes is the pupil of the eye. This circular aperture causes diffraction and the diffraction pattern falls on the retina of the eye as an image.

We have seen that the position for the first minimum for a single slit is given by the formula: $\theta = \dfrac{\lambda}{b}$

It has been shown (beyond this syllabus) that for a pupil of the human eye (a circular aperture) a similar formula can be applied to determine the minimum distance apart that two objects need to be to be resolvable (still seen as two objects). It is:

$$\theta = 1.22\dfrac{\lambda}{b} \ ,$$

where b is the diameter of the aperture (e.g. pupil) and θ is the angle, as shown in the diagram below:

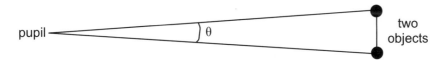

Maximum resolution power (minimum angle) given by $\theta = 1.22\dfrac{\lambda}{b}$ where b is pupil diameter (or other lens aperture, such as microscope).

Example T11.7

Two black dots with centres exactly 2mm apart, are drawn on a piece of white paper. How far back from the eyes can the paper be moved until the two dots are seen as one? (assume that the wavelength of light is 550 nm and that the pupil diameter is 2.5mm)

- Note that the angle, θ, must be in radians
- Note also that to solve the distance, you can either use $s = r\theta$ where r is distance from eyes to objects, s is distance between objects or you can use your own geometric solution based on the above triangle – the angles at the left end on above diagram can be assumed to be 90°.

Once you have solved this problem, try it out!

Practical Importance of resolution

Microscope and telescopes must be able to resolve separate images (example: cell walls). To change the resolving power one can only change the aperture size or the wavelength of light used. To increase resolving power one could use shorter wavelengths but one is limited since too short becomes not visible. Electron microscopes can be used – high energy, low wavelength electrons can be detected by sensors thus making them visible.

Very large apertures can also be used. Hence good quality telescope lenses typically have very diameters, as do radio telescopes (can be over 50m!).

Reading a CD or DVD involves shining light off pits on the disk. Sensors detect the light received, after reflection, and the information is then used to create sound, music etc. To be able to distinguish information from one pit to another, the pits must be resolvable. To increase the amount of information on a disk, the pits need to be small and close together. However, if they are too close they become unresolvable. Applying the Rayleigh criterion we see that we can increase the resolution power (and therefore be able to minimize pit size) by using light of very short wavelength. Short wavelength laser beams are thus used.

Polarization

Light is a member of the family of the electromagnetic spectrum.
Like all members of this family, it is an energy form that propagates (travels) at approximately $3 \times 10^8 ms^{-1}$ and consists of oscillating electric and magnetic fields. The oscillating electric field creates an oscillating magnetic field at right angles to the electric field, and the magnetic field creates an electric field and so on. This happens at "the speed of light". Both fields oscillate at right angles to the direction that the wave is travelling in – hence electromagnetic waves are classified as transverse waves.

The diagram below shows a simplified view of an electromagnetic wave:

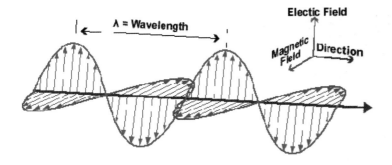

Copyright: ndt-ed.org

However, the diagram in fact shows an electromagnetic wave that has been plane polarized. A natural electromagnetic wave (e.g. light coming from a hot filament) consists of electric field oscillations in all directions perpendicular to the wave direction, and hence magnetic field directions are similarly distributed.

The following diagram shows some possible oscillations, to help illustrate this:

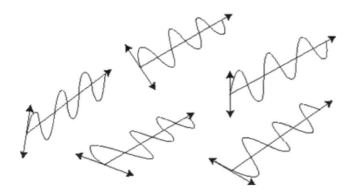

Copyright: iiviinfrared.com

Note that the diagrams only show the electric field oscillations ("vectors") – the magnetic ones would be perpendicular, as shown in the previous diagram.

Light (or any other electromagnetic radiation) that has been polarized has all but one plane of the electric field oscillations removed.

Special materials, called filters (polaroid filters) can do this – if light is passed through them it emerges as plane polarized light, as the following diagram shows:

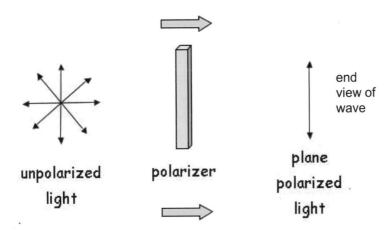

The following diagram shows another illustration of the same concept:

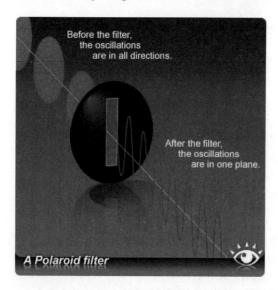

Copyright: learn.uci.edu

Malus's Law

If plane polarized light is passed through a Polaroid filter such as the above one, it passes through unaffected if the filter is orientated in the same plane as the light. Referring to the above diagram, if a second filter is placed in front of the one shown all the light will pass through unaffected (with unchanged intensity) as long as the second filter is still in line with the plane of the polarized light (So the "**transmission axis**" remains vertical). If the second filter is rotated through 90° it will completely stop the light. At other angles, the light will be reduced in **intensity** but not stopped.

The second filter in this example is referred to as an analyser, since it can be used to analyse/identify the plane of polarization of the light.

Malus's Law allows us to predict the intensity of such a beam of plane polarised light of initial intensity I_0 if the transmission axis is at an angle θ to the plane containing the electric field. The intensity of the transmitted light is given by I, where:

$I = I_0 cos^2 \theta$ Malus's Law

Malus's law can also be used to show that a Polaroid filter reduces the intensity of natural unpolarised light by 50%.

Polaroid sunglasses are therefore a useful way of reducing the glare and intensity of bright sunlight.

Example T11.8

Vertically polarized light falls on a polarizer that has its transmission axis at 30° to the vertical. By what percentage has the intensity of the light reduced in passing through the polarizer?

Polarization by reflection

When unpolarized light meets a surface such as water, where the light can both reflect and refract, the reflected ray is polarized to an extent. For example, the glare from the sea contains partially polarized light and this glare can be reduced by wearing Polaroid (polarizing) sunglasses. Depending on the angle of the sunglasses and the way that the light reaches the lens, the intensity of light can thus be cut down.

Brewster's Angle

I have stated that the reflected light is partially polarized. This means that more than one plane of the electric oscillation is still left. The extent of polarization depends on the angle that the incident ray makes with the reflecting surface. Brewster's angle gives the incident angle of the light required in order that the reflected light is totally polarized (i.e. plane polarized – all but one plane of electric field oscillations removed).

Brewsters angle occurs when the refracted ray is at 90° to the reflected ray, as shown in the diagram below:

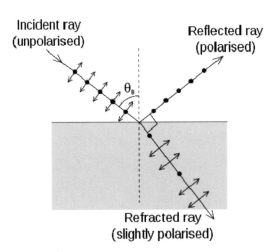

Brewster's law:

$$tan\theta_B = \frac{n_2}{n_1}$$

If the ray is incident in the air then

$n_1 = 1$ and $tan\theta_B = n_2$

n_2 is the refractive index of the medium (e.g. water)

Example T11.9

Calculate the angle between horizontal and a light ray incident on water if the light ray is to be totally polarized on reflection, given that the refractive index of water is 1.5

Optically active substances

Some substances are able to rotate the plane of plane polarized light. Such substances are called optically active substances. There are many optically active substances, including sugars and sweeteners. Light can be passed through solutions of such substances. The direction of the rotation depends on the chemical bonding in the substance and can be used to help identify the substance. The extent of the rotation depends on the concentration of the solution, and can thus be used to determine concentration (the angle of rotation of the plane polarized light is measured).

Stress Analysis

Materials under stress can also exhibit optical activity. Thus, if polarized light is shone on structures (such as metal tools, car windscreens) the way that the light is reflected can reveal stress points and possible weaknesses – in design or as a result of overstress due to loading.
LCD screens

Liquid Crystal Display (LCD) screens also make use of the polarisation of light. Each liquid crystal forms a pixel on the screen. Plane polarized light is passed through the liquid crystal. These crystals have the special property that they rotate the plane of polarised light by 90° but, if a voltage is applied to the crystal, they do not. Analyser filters are placed in front of the liquid crystals, so that only light that has the same axis of polarization as the incident light passes through. The crystals with no voltage applied rotate the light will therefore not allow the light to pass through and the crystals with voltage applied will allow light to pass through. It is not difficult to imagine that arrays of these crystals can be arranged to form digits (say, 0 to 9) and by applying the right voltage combinations any number can be illuminated.

Topic Twelve: Electromagnetic Induction

Electromotive force (emf) – an emf is a potential difference resulting from a source of electrical power. For example, the internal voltage, or potential difference supplied by a battery is referred to as its emf.

In this topic, the potential difference resulting from a conductor moving through a magnetic field is referred to as emf.

Induced emf or current – the word induced can be replaced with produced, but conventionally induced is the term used.

Emf (voltage) is induced in a wire if there is relative motion between the wire and a magnetic field. This can happen in one of several ways:

- if the wire/coil moves
- if the magnet or electromagnet moves
- if the electromagnet is switched on or off or is alternating

Note that emf (voltage) is only induced if field lines are "cut" by the wire/coil and that the rate of cutting determines the size of the emf induced.

Definition: **The induced emf is the amount of mechanical energy converted into electrical energy per unit charge.**

The unit of emf is the volt

Magnetic flux – a measure of the *amount* of field lines passing through an area, at right angles to that area – can be increased by increasing the area or the concentration (flux density) of field lines and is maximum when field lines are at right angles to area (component at right angles to the area decreases as field lines deviate from this angle).

Think of magnetic flux as the number of field lines and think of magnetic flux density as field strength

To understand the definition of magnetic flux density, remember that field strength is defined as the force per unit current length on a wire placed perpendicularly to the magnetic field. So it is essentially defined in terms of force.

Definition: **Magnetic Flux (Φ) (formula given in Data Book):**

$$\Phi = BA\cos\theta,$$

where

$B = magnetic\ field\ strength - Tesla\ (T)$

$A = area - square\ metres$

$\theta = angle\ between\ flux\ and\ line\ normal\ to\ area$

Unit: The weber (Wb) $1\,Wb = 1\,Tm^2$

Example T12.1

A coil of wire measuring 7.5cm by 11.5cm is placed between the poles of a magnet as follows:

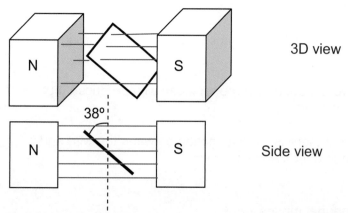

3D view

Side view

Find the magnetic flux passing through the coil, if the magnetic field between the poles of the magnet is 75mT

Magnetic Flux Linkage

Magnetic Flux Linkage - is a measure of the number of turns of wire "linked" to (passing through) magnetic flux. Can be increased by increasing magnetic flux or number of turns of wire.

Definition: *Flux linkage = flux × number of turns* $= \Phi \times N$

Example T12.2

If, in the previous example, the coil has 120 turns, find the flux linkage of the magnetic field through the coil

Note: Flux linkage has the same units as flux

Induced emf

Consider a wire moving through a uniform magnetic field, as follows:

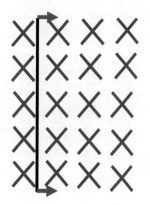

- The wire contains electrons free to move (free electrons).
- The movement of the wire from left to right means that the electrons within the wire also move from left to right.
- From previous work (chapter 5) we saw that charges moving within a magnetic field experience a force.
- The movement of the electrons, with the wire, from left to right, can be thought of as an electric current, from right to left (conventional)
- Using Fleming's Left Hand Rule (FLHR), we can predict a force on each electron down the wire (from top to bottom)
- This force on the electrons is the induced emf and a current will be induced in the wire, if allowed, from bottom to top (conventional current)

So, whenever a wire moves through a magnetic field, an emf is induced in the wire. The direction of the induced current can be determined using the method described above, but it is easier using Fleming's Right Hand Rule (FRHR)

The thumb and fingers of the **Right Hand** are arranged as follows:

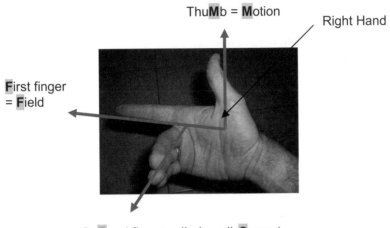

SeCond finger = (Induced) Current

Notes
- if conductor moves through a magnetic field parallel to the field lines, no emf is induced; there must be a component of the field perpendicular to the movement of the conductor.
- As a conductor moves through a magnetic field, field lines (flux) are said to be cut.
- The size of the induced emf is dependent on the rate at which field lines are cut

Example T12.3

An emf is induced across the wings of an aircraft as it takes off and continues on its flight-path. Give two reasons why the induced emf may be greater during the aircraft's flight-path than during take-off.

Faraday's Law

The induced emf (ε) in a circuit is equal to the rate of change of flux linkage through the circuit.

$$\varepsilon = -\frac{\Delta(N\Phi)}{\Delta t} = -N\frac{\Delta\Phi}{\Delta t} \; (given \; in \; data \; book)$$

gradient of $N\Phi$ versus t graph   gradient of Φ versus t graph

Note;
- The minus sign indicates that the emf is always induced so as to oppose the change causing it – see Lenz's law.
- Flux linkage changes if a wire or a coil moves through a magnetic field (area cut multiplied by turns) or if a coil spins or moves in a magnetic field.

Derivation: emf induced in a straight conductor moving through a uniform magnetic field

Faraday's law can be applied to a straight conductor moving through a uniform magnetic field at right angles to the field, as follows:

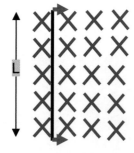

Let:
Strength of field = B
Area swept out per second = A
Length of wire in contact with field = L,
Wire move through field at speed v

$$\frac{\Delta \Phi}{\Delta t} = \frac{\Delta(BA)}{\Delta t} \; Since \; \Phi = BA\cos 90 = BA$$

$$B\frac{\Delta A}{\Delta t} \; (since \; B \; is \; constant)$$

$$= B\frac{L \times d}{\Delta t} \; (where \; d = distance \; moved)$$

$$= BL\frac{\Delta d}{\Delta t} \; (since \; L \; is \; constant)$$

$$= BLv \left(\frac{\Delta d}{\Delta t} = speed \right)$$

For a wire moving through a magnetic field, at speed v, at right angles to the field, strength B, the induced emf, ε, is given by:

$$\varepsilon = BLv$$

Example T12.4

A horizontal steel rod of length 235mm is dropped horizontally through a magnetic field of strength 45mT and direction horizontal and at right angles to the rod. Find the size of the induced emf after (a) 0.1 second (b) 0.5 seconds, assuming g=10ms^{-2} and that the rod remains in the field as it drops, and remains horizontal.

Example T12.5

A 35 turn rectangular coil, measuring 5.0cm by 8.5cm is moved through a uniform 35mT magnetic field at a speed of 10 cms^{-1}, as shown in the diagram below:

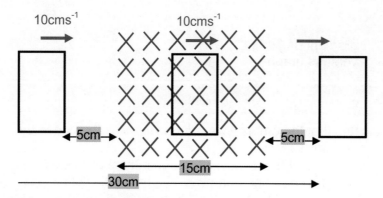

(a) Describe the motion of the electrons and the current in the coil as the coil:

    (i) begins to enter the magnetic field
    (ii) moves totally within the magnetic field
    (iii) begins to move out of the magnetic field, on the right hand side

(b) Calculate the maximum current in the coil, assuming that the resistance of the coil is 0.01Ω and explain where the coil is in order to attain this maximum current

(c) Sketch a graph showing how the current on the bottom edge of the coil varies with distance moved by the coil, as it moves forward 30cm, as shown in the diagram.

Lenz's Law

The direction of the induced current (or emf) is always so as to oppose the change causing it.

Lenz's law is an application of the principle of conservation of energy. If Lenz's law did not apply, energy could be made from nothing.
Consider, for example, moving a bar magnet into a cylindrical coil, with the North end entering first, as follows:

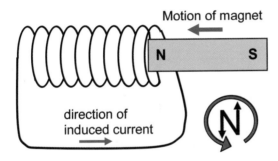

- The magnet is pushed into the coil.
- This movement is the change causing the induced current.
- The direction of the induced current will be so as to oppose this motion
- A north pole will therefore be induced on the right hand end of the coil (to repel the magnet)
- This corresponds to an anti-clockwise current (see diagram below magnet) as viewed from this end of the coil.
- The current in the coil is therefore as indicated on the diagram.

Note that if a S pole was induced on the coil-end, the magnet would be attracted into the coil, so it would move faster into the coil, a greater induced current would result, and electrical energy would be created out of nothing. As it is, in order to induce current, a force has to be applied to overcome repulsion and work done against this force equals electrical energy induced in the coil. Energy is conserved.

Using similar arguments, as the coil is pulled out, an attractive S pole will be induced on the right hand end of the coil, and current will flow in the opposite direction.

In many instances Lenz's law or FRHR can be used to predict the direction of the induced current. However, the Lenz's Law method is often simpler and easier to use.

Example T12.6

A long straight wire is in the same plane as a rectangular loop of metallic wire. The straight wire carries a current, I as shown, and is moved towards the rectangular loop. What happens to the loop of wire?

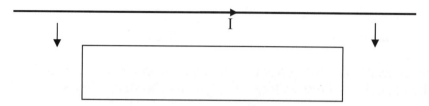

Alternating Current

Electricity is generated by using a primary source of energy to turn turbines which in turn rotates coils of wire in magnetic fields. This form of electricity generation results in an alternating emf, that varies sinusoidally. Hence our domestic electricity is not dc (direct current) but alternating, with a frequency of 50 Hz (50 cycles per second) in the United Kingdom and many other countries.

To understand this, consider a simple ac generator:

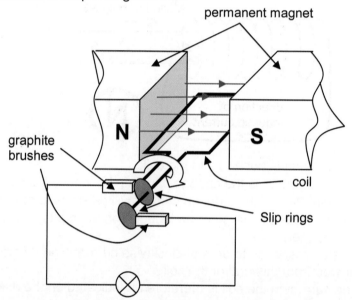

The ac generator is very much like a motor, except that instead of current being fed into the coil and the coil interacting with the magnetic field and turning, the coil is made to turn through a magnetic field and this results in current being induced in the coil.

Consider the coil in its current position:

- If it is made to rotate clockwise (as viewed from in front of the page)
- The left hand side of the coil moves upwards
- Using FRHR, current is induced in the wire on this side into the page
- The right hand side of the coil moves downwards
- Using FRHR, current is induced in the wire on this side out of the page, towards the observer.
- The current through the bulb will be moving from right to left (←)

However, as the coil continues to rotate, the direction of the current changes. As it is moving at 90° from its current position, there will in fact be zero current induced in the coil. At this position, the wires (at top and bottom of coil, in this position) are not cutting field lines, but moving along them.

Consider the following end-on diagrams of the side of the coil moving through the magnetic flux:

The sides of the coil are represented by the marks (•). These wires are the ones that move through the magnetic field and where emf is induced. The size of the induced emf depends on the rate at which the flux is cut.

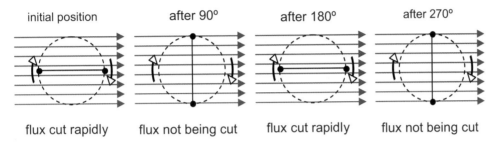

As viewed from the front (generator diagram), current is always induced into the page. However, every 180°, the wires swap over the brush that they feed into. This results in a reversal of direction of current every 180°.

To show this, we can look at the relevant parts of the generator as it turns through 180°:

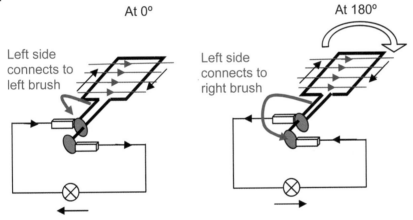

A current-time graph thus reveals the sinuisoidal emf (and current) that results in the coil: Time corresponds to angle of coil, since the coil rotates at a constant speed.

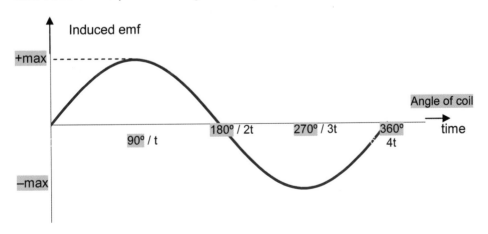

Note that the maximum flux change (rate of cutting flux) is when the coil is parallel to the field – this may seem confusing, but refer to the four diagrams above and count how many field lines are cut in the top 45° sector of the coil's rotation path (≈ 0) and compare this with the number cut in a 45° sector at either the left or right of the centre of the circle ($\approx 3 \; or \; 4$).

Note also that if the rotation frequency of the coil is doubled, the peaks on the above graph occur twice as often and the maximum (peak) emf is twice as high – so the graph will have twice the amplitude

Power of a.c. current & voltage.

Direct current (d.c.) is current that always flows in the same direction. Electrical supplies that produce d.c. current usually produce current that is not only in a constant direction, but also of a constant size.

For example, $3A \; d.c \Rightarrow$ current is a constant value of $3A$.
So what does $3A \; a.c$ mean?

To run many electrical appliances, either a.c. or d.c. electricity may be used. For example, a 60 watt light bulb appears to be identical in brightness whether run on a.c. or d.c. (as long as the correct voltage is used in both instances)

The problem is that the voltage of an a.c. supply varies from negative to zero to positive. One could quote the maximum positive voltage, as the voltage of an a.c. supply. If we do this, then compare running a bulb with 50V d.c. with 50V a.c. Clearly the 50V d.c. supply would supply a higher amount of energy to the bulb, since it remains at 50V, whilst the a.c. supply varies, producing a lower average rate of energy-supply, and resulting in a dimmer bulb.

There is another, more useful way of measuring a.c. voltage and current.

Consider a supply that produces an alternating voltage, with maximum (peak) value, 2V. Suppose that this results in a current of peak value 1A. The current produced by a sinuisoidal a.c. voltage is also sinuisoidal, as long as the conductor is ohmic (in which case, $V \propto I$)

This is represented on the graph below – the red line represents current and the green line; voltage.

The average current, if one wished to find it, is clearly zero, and the average voltage is zero. However, since $power = current \times voltage$ and $negative \times negative = positive$, power is always positive. When the current and voltage as shown in the graph are multiplied together, the result is the blue line, representing power.

Current, voltage and power in an a.c. circuit - graph

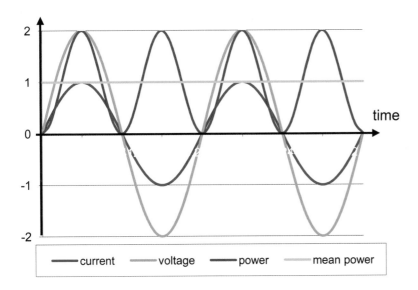

One can see intuitively from the graph that the average power is half peak (maximum) power, 1 watt, in this case. Maximum power is 2 watts, and minimum power is 0 watts, so power also varies. With mains appliances, voltage and current change direction so rapidly that the maximum and zero power are not observed – one does not see the bulb dim and brighten (in fact, the bulb would not have time to cool down). The average power is observed.

So average power of an a.c. supply is equal to half peak power.
This leads us to the concept of root-mean-square current and voltage:

I'll start by defining the problem: imagine an a.c. circuit , of resistance R, that has a peak supply voltage equal to V_0 which results in a peak a.c. current of I_0. We want to find the equivalent d.c. voltage and equivalent d.c. current that will deliver the same power as the a.c. circuit.

power = current × voltage

peak power (P_0) = *peak current × peak voltage* = $I_0 V_0$

average power = $\frac{1}{2}$ *peak power* = $\frac{1}{2}(I_0 V_0)$

But $V = I \times R \Rightarrow V_0 = I_0 R \;\Rightarrow\; I_0 = \dfrac{V_0}{R}$

$\therefore$ *average power* $= \frac{1}{2}(I_0(I_0 R)) = \frac{1}{2}I_0^2 R = \frac{1}{2}\left(\dfrac{V_0}{R}\right)V_0 = \frac{1}{2}\dfrac{V_0^2}{R}$

so we have four possible expressions for average power:

average power $= \frac{1}{2}P_0$

average power $= \frac{1}{2}(I_0 V_0)$

average power $= \frac{1}{2}I_0^2 R$

average power $= \frac{1}{2}\dfrac{V_0^2}{R}$

Now to find the d.c. voltage and current. Suppose the voltage required to produce the same power as the average power calculated above is V and the current, I

$Power = V \times I$, but $V = I \times R$ ∴ $Power = (I \times R) \times I = I^2 R$

or, $I = V/R$ ∴ $Power = V \times V/R = \dfrac{V^2}{R}$

Equating d.c. power to a.c. power, we get:

$$I^2\cancel{R} = \tfrac{1}{2}I_0^2\cancel{R} \Rightarrow I^2 = \tfrac{1}{2}I_0^2 \Rightarrow I = \sqrt{\tfrac{1}{2}I_0^2} = \dfrac{I_0}{\sqrt{2}}$$

and, $\dfrac{V^2}{\cancel{R}} = \tfrac{1}{2}\dfrac{V_0^2}{\cancel{R}} \Rightarrow V^2 = \tfrac{1}{2}V_0^2 \Rightarrow V = \sqrt{\tfrac{1}{2}V_0^2} = \dfrac{V_0}{\sqrt{2}}$

We call the d.c. voltage and current required to give the same power as the average (mean) power produced by peak voltage and current of V_0 and I_0 the rms (root mean square) voltage and current, and give them the symbols, V_{rms} and I_{rms}

Hence: $I_{rms} = \dfrac{I_0}{\sqrt{2}}$ and $V_{rms} = \dfrac{V_0}{\sqrt{2}}$

Example T12.7

A bulb is usually powered with an a.c. supply with a peak emf of 12V. What d.c. voltage would be required to power the bulb with equal brightness?

Example T12.8

In the U.K. mains electricity is alternating at 50Hz, and has rms voltage of 240V. What is the maximum voltage produced by a U.K mains supply?

Example T12.9

An electric heater designed for use for the U.K. mains supply, (a.c, 240V,rms), is rated as 2000W.

(a) What is the rms current through the heating element when connected to the mains?
(b) What is the maximum current when connect to the mains?
(c) What is the resistance of the heating element?
(d) If the heater is run on an a.c. supply with a peak voltage of 240V, how will this affect the power of the heater?

Transmission of Electrical Power

Transformers

Transformers make use of electromagnetic induction, but also allow voltage to be increased or decreased without significant loss of power. Transformers basically consist of 2 coils of wire. The first coil, called the primary coil, is powered by an a.c. electrical supply. Electro-motive-force (voltage) is induced in the other (secondary) coil. This induced voltage and current is caused by expanding or collapsing field lines caused by the changing current in the primary coil (supply is alternating). The field is therefore continually cut by wires in the secondary coil.

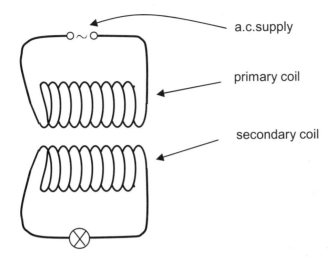

a.c.supply

primary coil

secondary coil

The voltage induced in the secondary coil depends on the turns in the primary and secondary coil and on the voltage across the primary coil so by altering the turns ratio for the two coils, the voltage in the secondary can be changed from that provided by the supply (in the primary coil).

Equation:

$$\frac{V_p}{V_s} = \frac{N_p}{N_s}, \text{ where,}$$

V_p = voltage in primary coil, V_s = voltage in secondary coil

N_p = turns in primary coil, N_s = turns in secondary coil

Transformers which increase the supply voltage are called **step up transformers** and those which reduce it are called **step down transformers**.

Example T12.10

A transformer has been designed to convert voltage from 240V to 12V. If the secondary coil has 125 turns, how many turns should the primary coil have? (assume transformer is 100% efficient)

Obviously, if voltage is increased, there must be a decrease in current, (so that power is same in both coils) otherwise energy would be created.

If transformers are completely efficient in transferring energy from one coil to the other then,

Power used in primary coil   = power produced in secondary

$$\Rightarrow V_p I_p = V_s I_s$$

$$\Rightarrow \frac{V_p}{V_s} = \frac{I_s}{I_p}, \text{ and } \frac{N_p}{N_s} = \frac{I_s}{I_p}$$

Ideal Transformer – construction

Transformers are never 100% efficient, but they are designed to be as close as possible to "ideal" (100% efficient). They are constructed, as follows:

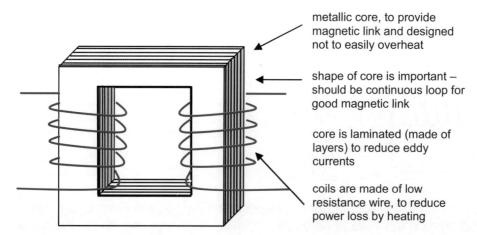

metallic core, to provide magnetic link and designed not to easily overheat

shape of core is important – should be continuous loop for good magnetic link

core is laminated (made of layers) to reduce eddy currents

coils are made of low resistance wire, to reduce power loss by heating

Note: Eddy current are currents induced in the core which try to oppose and reduce the current induced in the wire. Laminating the core makes it difficult to conduct electricity without changing significantly the magnetic linkage properties of the core.

Power Transmission

Transformers are hugely useful in the National Grid system of electricity distribution, since the transfer of electricity is more efficient at high voltage and low current than at high current and low voltage (high current leads to a high level of energy loss by heating – as a consequence of resistance in the transporting wires).

Transformers are thus used to increase voltages at power stations for transport over the grid. They are employed again to decrease voltages to the appropriate level at the users end of the network. The power lost as heat in the wires is given by:

Power Loss = I^2R where I is the current and R is the total resistance of the wires used.

Example T12.11

A factory requires electrical energy at a rate of 20MW. If the resistance of the electricity cable used to transport electricity to the factory is $4.8\,\Omega$, calculate the power losses in the cable if the supply voltage is: (a) 100kV (b) 10kV

The example demonstrates that increasing the current in the cable by a factor of 10 causes a 100-fold increase in power-loss. Therefore using high voltage and low current electricity transmission (particularly over long distances) is far better than using low voltage and high current.

Risks and Concerns

Being in the presence of power lines or electrical appliances can cause the induction of tiny currents in the human body. However, it seems unlikely that low frequency magnetic fields such as these cause any harm to the human body. Further study is necessary: currently we have no conclusive evidence.

Topic Thirteen: Quantum Physics and Nuclear Physics

Quantum Physics

This topic discusses the fact that light can be considered as particles (each with a quantum of energy called a photon) and also as waves, where the energy is continuous and unbroken).

In more general terms, the so called "wave particle duality" considers that what we normally consider as waves (like light, X rays etc.) can behave like particles and what we usually consider as particles (like electrons) can behave like waves.

The photoelectric effect is one experimental effect that shows light behaves like particles:

The Photoelectric Effect

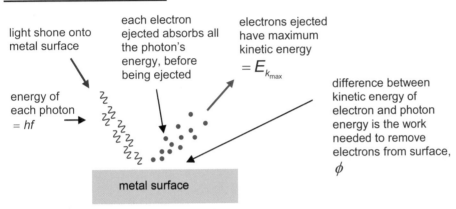

light shone onto metal surface

each electron ejected absorbs all the photon's energy, before being ejected

electrons ejected have maximum kinetic energy $= E_{k_{max}}$

energy of each photon $= hf$

difference between kinetic energy of electron and photon energy is the work needed to remove electrons from surface, ϕ

metal surface

This is the effect whereby if light is shone onto a metal surface, electrons (called photoelectrons) are emitted.

- electrons are only emitted if the light is above a certain frequency, called the threshold frequency (ultra-violet light is needed for some metals)
- the value of this threshold frequency depends on the metal being used

  and, assuming the frequency of the light is above threshold frequency:

- the number of photoelectrons emitted depends on the intensity of the light
- the photoelectrons emitted have a range of kinetic energies, up to a certain maximum value (and this maximum kinetic energy depends on the metal used and the frequency of light).

This is explained by the fact that free electrons each require a certain amount of energy to escape from the surface of the metal.

- the minimum energy required to release an electron from a certain metal is called the work function (ϕ) of the metal

Further, it is necessary to consider that the light hitting the metal behaves as particles (photons), rather than continuous waves.

- if light behaved as a wave then, even at low frequency the light would eventually provide enough energy to release an electron. This is not the case

So the energy comes from a particle of light. When a "light particle", (called a photon) hits an electron, it gives up all of its energy to the electron

- the energy of each photon depends on the frequency of the light

Each photon has energy given by the equation: $E = hf$

- E is energy, in joules, h is Planck's constant, $6.63 \times 10^{-34}\,Js$ and f is the frequency of the light

If the work function of the metal is greater than the photon energy (ie. if light frequency is too low), then no photoelectrons will be emitted

- $hf < \phi \Rightarrow no\ emission$

The minimum frequency required to just release photons from the metal is called the threshold frequency - f_0, and the photon energy at this frequency is therefore equal to the work function of the metal

- $hf_0 = \phi$

If the frequency is above threshold frequency, then electrons (with kinetic energy) are emitted

- $f > f_0 \Rightarrow hf > hf_0 \Rightarrow hf > \phi \Rightarrow emission\ results$

Since an electron absorbs all of a photon's energy then if photon energy is greater than energy required to release electron (work function), electron will not only be released, but will have kinetic energy. The kinetic energy will be equal to the amount of energy provided by the photon, over and above the energy required to release it. This is the maximum kinetic energy of the electron since it may have required a little more energy than the work function, (work function is minimum energy required) to escape.

- $E_{k_{max}} = hf - \phi \Rightarrow hf = \phi + E_{k_{max}}$

(This equation was derived by Einstein who explained the photoelectric effect, as above)

Example T13.1

Light is shone onto a potassium surface and the frequency is gradually increased until, when the frequency is just above $5.38 \times 10^{14}\,Hz$, photoelectrons are emitted from the surface. The frequency is then increased to $5.95 \times 10^{14}\,Hz$.

(a) calculate the work function of potassium, in electron volts.
(b) calculate the maximum speed of the photoelectrons when the higher frequency light is applied.

Stopping Potential

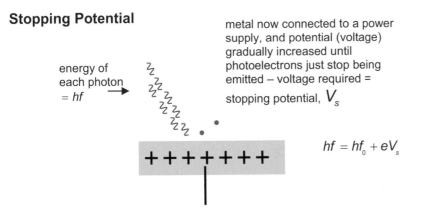

energy of each photon = hf $\longrightarrow$

metal now connected to a power supply, and potential (voltage) gradually increased until photoelectrons just stop being emitted – voltage required = stopping potential, V_s

$$hf = hf_0 + eV_s$$

If the metal surface is given a positive charge it will attract back the electrons, making it more difficult for them to escape.

The energy required to "move" an electron through a potential difference of V volts, or put another way, the energy required to increase the potential of an electron by V volts, is given by the equation $W = qV$. Since we are talking about electrons, $q = e$ and therefore, $W = eV$.

So, in order to remove an electron from a metal surface with a (positive) potential, V, the energy of the photon has to be sufficient to overcome the work function of the metal and to increase the potential of the electron, for it to escape the attraction of the metal.

Conversely, if a frequency above threshold frequency is used, so that, under normal circumstances, electrons would escape with additional kinetic energy and the potential of the metal is gradually raised until photoelectric emission just stops, then this potential is called stopping potential – symbol V_s

Summary:

energy available by photons = hf (photon energy)

minimum energy required to release electrons (no potential) = ϕ (work function) = hf_0

where minimum frequency of light = f_0 (threshold frequency)

additional energy available for E_k = $hf - \phi = hf - hf_0$

If stopping potential, V_s applied to metal, $eV = hf - hf_0 \Rightarrow hf = hf_0 + eV_s$ and electrons can no longer escape (kinetic energy is reduced to zero)

Equations (given in data book)

$E = hf$ to find photon energy of incident radiation (light)

$hf = \phi + E_{k\,max}$ to find kinetic energy of photoelectrons

$hf = hf_0 + eV_s$ to find stopping potential ($E_{k_{max}} = 0$)

This last equation tells us that stopping potential depends on the threshold frequency (which depends on the metal surface) and on the frequency of the incident radiation.

Example T13.2

(a) Calculate the stopping potential for the potassium surface, as in T12.1, when the high frequency light, as in (b) is used.
(b) calculate the stopping potential when ultra-violet light, of wavelength 375nm is used as the incident radiation.

Graphical

If, for a certain metal, the stopping potential is measured for various frequencies of incident radiation, the following graph is obtained:

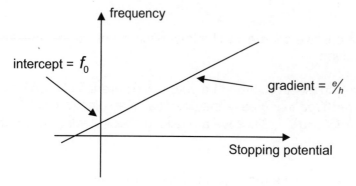

We get a straight line graph, because the relationship between stopping potential and frequency is linear – as shown by the equation:

$$hf = hf_0 + eV_s$$
$$\Rightarrow f = \frac{hf_0 + eV_s}{h} = f_0 + \frac{e}{h}V_s$$
$$\therefore f = \frac{e}{h}V_s + f_0$$

Comparing this with the formula of a general straight line, $y = mx + c$, we see that the gradient of the line is equal to $\frac{e}{h}$ and the y-axis intercept, f_0

Wave-particle duality

We have seen that waves behave as particles (e.g. photoelectric effect). It has also been shown that what we usually consider to be particles show wave-like behaviour.

de Broglie's Hypothesis

de Broglie suggested that all (moving) particles have a wave like nature. He linked the wavelength (so called de Broglie wavelength) with the momentum of the particle in the following equation:

$$\lambda = \frac{h}{p} \Rightarrow p = \frac{h}{\lambda}, \text{ where, }$$

$p = momentum\ of\ particle$
$h = Planck's\ constant$
$\lambda = (de\ Broglie)\ wavelength\ of\ particle$

Validation

de Broglie's theory was tested by directing electrons at a thin metal foil. It was shown that the electrons were diffracted to form a pattern of rings on a screen – the same pattern as that produced by X-rays.

Electrons are usually considered as particles and diffraction is wave behaviour. Therefore de Broglie was proven right: particles do behave as waves.

Example T13.3

Find the de Broglie wavelength of a beam of electrons moving at $2.5 \times 10^5 ms^{-1}$

Example T13.4

Find the speed of electrons necessary for an electron beam to behave like x-rays, of frequency $3.4 \times 10^{18} Hz$

Atomic Spectra and Energy States – Bohr's Postulates

We saw in Topic 7 how atomic emission and absorption spectra arise. We shall now look in more detail at the processes involved.

Remember, the spectra arise because of electron energy level jumps from one shell (allowed electron energy state) to another. Bohr made some suggestions (postulates) that can be used to quantify some of these energy transitions.

Bohr's Postulates

1. Only certain levels - orbits/energies are allowed for the electrons in an atom – called stationary states or quantum levels.
2. The electron will not radiate (or absorb) energy whilst in one of these states.
3. During a (quantum) jump, energy transfer is given by, $E = hf$, where E is the energy, in joules, f is the frequency of radiation emitted or absorbed and h is Planck's constant.

Consider, for example, the hydrogen atom.

The lowest energy state for its electron is the first shell, called $n = 1$
This lowest, most stable energy state, is called the ground state.
In order to jump from the ground state to higher states, energy is needed. If hydrogen is illuminated with the whole spectrum of frequencies of electro-magnetic radiation, the photons with the correct energy to cause this excitation from the ground state to the next state ($n = 2$) will be absorbed. Other photons will be absorbed when they pass on their energies to promote the electron between other energy states (shells). This is how an absorption spectrum arises.

The energy levels for the hydrogen atom are as follows:

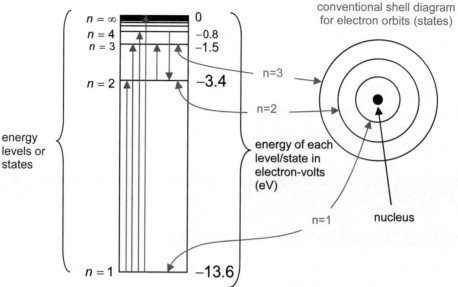

energy level diagram showing
energy levels and transitions

conventional shell diagram
for electron orbits (states)

energy levels or states

energy of each level/state in electron-volts (eV)

nucleus

Notes:

- The blue lines represent some of the possible transitions from one state (or level) to another.
- Transitions can occur from any state to any other state
- States $n = 5, 6, etc$ have not been shown, for lack of space!
- $n = \infty$ corresponds to the electron entirely leaving the atom – ionization
- For a transition of the electron from $n = 1$ to a higher level, energy must be put in (absorbed from electromagnetic radiation, if available)
- If the electron drops, atom will emit energy (in the form of electromagnetic radiation)
- The type of electromagnetic radiation absorbed or emitted depends on the size of the energy transition (and hence frequency of photon)
- Different atoms have different energy levels – this is why absorption and emission spectra can be used to identify materials.

Example T13.5

(a) Using the diagram above page find the energy required, in joules, to ionize a hydrogen atom from its ground state
(b) Hence, find the frequency of electromagnetic radiation to effect this transition.

Example T13.6

A hydrogen line emission spectrum has a line of wavelength $1.78 \times 10^{-6} m$.
(a) Find the photon energy, in eV, of light emitted for this line
(b) Using the energy level diagram above, identify the transition causing this line

The diagram below shows the emission spectrum for hydrogen. The lines are all in the visible range. They correspond to transitions to the level $n = 2$, from other levels. The highest energy light emitted is the blue light on the far left, and the lowest is the red (red has lower frequency than blue light). Hence the lines on the left correspond to larger electron transitions than those on the right.

Emission spectrum for hydrogen

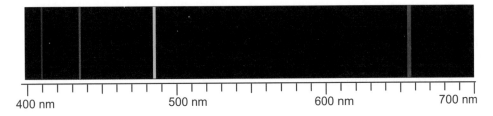

400 nm   500 nm   600 nm   700 nm

Example T13.7

Using the energy level diagram for hydrogen, shown two pages previously, identify the transitions for two of the lines in the hydrogen emission spectrum shown above (do all for more practice, if you wish!!) [Note that the energy levels shown are approximate so your answers will not agree exactly to the lines shown on the emission spectrum].

Electron in a Box Model

The electron in a box model considers that an electron has certain possible wavelengths, determined by standing waves that fit in the box exactly like standing waves on a string. It explains why atomic electrons only have certain discreet energies. The model provides the following formula for energies:

$$E_K = \frac{n^2 h^2}{8 m_e L^2}$$ where: $n = 1,2,3,\dots$ $h = Plank's\ constant,$ $m_e = mass\ of\ an\ electron,$

$$L = length\ of\ the\ box$$

Schrodinger's Model of electrons within the atom

Schrodinger's model basically did not predict exactly where an electron is in an atom, but it provided a mathematical probability function defining the region where it is, say 95%, likely to be. It theorized that in fact an electron position cannot be found, or predicted with certainty, but the region for 95% certainty is actually quite small. These "probability regions" are called orbitals and his theory is still used to define various shapes of electron orbitals. His model has helped scientists understand chemical bonding and molecular structure.

Heisenberg's Uncertainty Principle

This principle states that it is impossible to know with certainty:

- both the position and the momentum of a particle

- both the time elapsed and the energy of a particle

Note that it is possible to know with certainty one of the pairs, for example position, but if this is the case the other (e.g. momentum) is not known at all.

Nuclear Physics

Nuclear Size

One method of finding the approximate size of a nucleus is from the results of Gieger & Marsden's alpha scattering experiment – as described in Topic 7. Please review this experiment before continuing.

The information we need from this experiment is that if alpha particles are directed at a gold foil about $6.0 \times 10^{-7} m$ thick, one in 8000 are deflected by angles greater than 90°. As explained earlier, we assume that deflections of this kind can only occur when the alpha particle hits one of the gold nuclei and "bounces" back.

For this approximation we also need to know the approximate size of an atom. This can be found by accurate density measurements (details not required) and the diameter of an atom is found to be approximately $3.0 \times 10^{-10} m$

Now let's define some variables:

$$
\begin{aligned}
D_N &= diameter\ of\ a\ nucleus \\
D_A &= diameter\ of\ an\ atom\ (= 3 \times 10^{-10} m) \\
A_N &= cross\ sectional\ area\ of\ a\ nucleus \\
A_A &= cross\ sectional\ area\ of\ an\ atom
\end{aligned}
$$

Let:

We consider a single layer of the gold atoms:

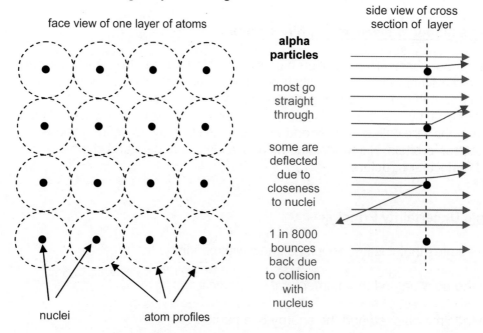

face view of one layer of atoms

side view of cross section of layer

alpha particles

most go straight through

some are deflected due to closeness to nuclei

1 in 8000 bounces back due to collision with nucleus

nuclei   atom profiles

The number of layers, n, of gold atoms in the $0.6 \mu m$ gold foil is equal to the thickness of the foil divided by the diameter of one atom.

$$ n = \frac{6 \times 10^{-7} m}{3 \times 10^{-10} m} = 2000 $$

Since alpha particles are only deflected by the gold nuclei (and not the rest of the atom),

the proportion of alpha particles deflected by one layer of gold nuclei $= \dfrac{area\ of\ nuclei\ in\ one\ layer}{area\ of\ atoms\ in\ one\ layer}$

(the atoms are so small that they effectively fill up all space in the layer)

$$= \dfrac{cross\ sectional\ area\ of\ a\ nucleus}{cross\ sectional\ area\ of\ an\ atom} \quad (same\ ratio)$$

$$= \dfrac{A_N}{A_A}$$

proportion of alpha particles deflected by 2000 layers (ie by the gold foil) $= 2000 \times \dfrac{A_N}{A_A}$

but we know that the foil deflects 1 alpha particle in 8000 hence:

$$\dfrac{1}{8000} = 2000 \times \dfrac{A_N}{A_A}$$

$$, \Rightarrow A_N = \dfrac{A_A}{8000 \times 2000}$$

$$\Rightarrow \pi \dfrac{D_N^2}{4} = \dfrac{\pi D_A^2 / 4}{8000 \times 2000} = \dfrac{\pi D_A^2}{4 \times 8000 \times 2000} \quad \left(\pi r^2 = \pi \dfrac{D^2}{4} \right)$$

$$\Rightarrow D_N^2 = \dfrac{D_A^2}{16000000}$$

$$But,\ D_A = 3 \times 10^{-10}\ m \Rightarrow D_N^2 = \dfrac{(3 \times 10^{-10})^2}{16000000} = 5.63 \times 10^{-27}$$

$$\Rightarrow D_N = \sqrt{5.63 \times 10^{-14}} = 7.5 \times 10^{-14}$$

So, using this method, we see that an approximation of the diameter of a nucleus is $7.5 \times 10^{-14}\ m$, and that an atom is about 10^4 times the size (diameter) of a nucleus.

Nuclear mass

The mass spectrometer is particularly useful for comparing masses of various molecular fragments. They are used extensively in organic chemistry to identify organic molecules. The sample is first bombarded with electrons. This causes the molecules to fragment (split) into neutral and positive ions.

For example, if the sample was propane, propane has the formula CH_3–CH_2–CH_3 (C_3H_8). Possible fragments are C^+, CH^+, CH_2^+, CH_3^+, CH_3–CH_2^+, etc. The relative mass of these fragments is 12 (for C^+), 13 (12+1 for CH^+), 14, 15, and 29. The mass spectrometer tells us the mass of these fragments, and from this information (usually with other information aswell) we can deduce that the original sample is propane.

The principle of a mass spectrometer is that the ions are deflected by a magnetic field and the amount of deflection depends on the mass of each fragment (ion) and on the charge.

Mass Spectrometer – schematic diagram

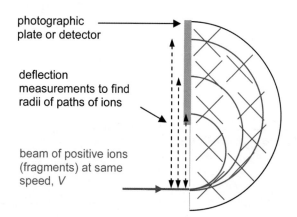

photographic plate or detector

deflection measurements to find radii of paths of ions

beam of positive ions (fragments) at same speed, V

red crosses in semi-circular area show presence of uniform magnetic field going into page

blue semicircles show paths of ions with different masses and/or charges

Notes

- the positive ions are accelerated using an electric field and are passed through a velocity selector, which ensures they all have the same velocity when they enter the mass magnetic field, shown above.
- all charged particles travel in circles when moving through, and at right angles to, a uniform magnetic field.
- usually the particles will all have the same charge; +1, but they could for example be ions with a +2 charge.
- Using FLHR we can predict the direction of the force on the positive charges as they enter, and travel through the magnetic field – remember, direction of conventional current is in the same direction as positive charge. On the point of entry, the force is thus upwards, and as they move, the force is always at right angles to the velocity of the particles, towards the centre of the circle that they describe.

Theory

magnetic force on ions = centripetal force required to maintain them in a circle

$$\Rightarrow Bqv = \frac{mv^2}{r}, \quad \text{where,}$$

B = magnetic field strength
q = charge on ion
v = speed of ion
m = mass of ion
r = radius of path in magnetic field

$$\Rightarrow \frac{m}{q} = \frac{Bvr}{v^2} \Rightarrow \frac{m}{q} = \frac{Br}{v} \Rightarrow \frac{m}{q} = \frac{B}{v}r$$

and, since B and v are constant, $\frac{m}{q} \propto r$

for singly charged ions, $q = e$, and $m \propto r$

So we can measure the radius of the path taken by the various ions and find their mass ratios. If the field strength and velocity of particles is known, we can find their actual masses (mass:charge ratio)

The mass spectrometer provides evidence for isotopes, since it identifies species of the same element that have atoms of different mass.

Example T13.8

Hydrogen ions are passed through a mass spectrometer and it is found that two paths of different radii are taken to the deflector plate. Explain this observation.

Example T13.9

Two particles, X^+ and Y^{2+}, enter a mass spectrometer. The mass of Y is triple (3x) the mass of X. If the radius of the path taken through the magnetic field in the mass spectrometer by X^+ is R, find, in terms of R, the radius of the path taken by Y^{2+}

Nuclear Energy Levels

Experimental evidence shows that nuclei, not only atoms, have certain energy levels. One example of such evidence is during radioactive decay processes. When a parent nucleus undergoes radioactive decay, the decay product, or daughter nucleus, is usually in an excited state. It relaxes back to its ground state by emitting a gamma-ray photon. The fact that a gamma ray photon is emitted is evidence for the fact that the nucleus can be in an excited, high energy state. Further, certain nuclei only emit photons of a certain frequency (and, therefore, energy) – the photon energy is observed to be characteristic of the nucleus. This is evidence for the fact that nuclei have well-defined energy levels, as do atoms (and their "electron shells").

Radioactive Decay

Beta Decay

There are 3 types of beta decay: electron emission, positron emission and electron capture. We only consider the first two.

Electron emission

Electron emission occurs when a nucleus is unstable due to the high neutron:proton ratio, and resulting instability A neutron within the nucleus changes into a proton and an electron. The proton remains within the nucleus, but the electron is ejected, as a beta-particle.

Example T13.10

Carbon-14 (atomic number, 6) decays to Nitrogen-14 (atomic, number, 7), with emission of another radiation. Explain this process by reference to the neutron:proton ratio of the two nuclei and write a nuclear reaction equation to illustrate it. Name the radiation emission.

Positron Emission

A positron is the anti-particle of an electron. It has the same mass and charge of an electron, except that the charge is positive and not negative. Symbol: $^0_1 e$ or β^+

Positron emission occurs when a nucleus is unstable due to the high proton:neutron ratio, and resulting instability A proton within the nucleus changes into a neutron and a positron. The neutron remains within the nucleus, but the positron is ejected – as a positive beta-particle.

Example T13.11

Complete the nuclear reaction equation by filling in the mass and atomic number for Neon. Explain why the decay has occurred and name the emission.

$$^{22}_{11}Na \rightarrow \quad Ne + {}^{0}_{1}e$$

Notes
- There are no naturally occurring positron emitters – for example, sodium-22 is not naturally occurring – it must be created by another nuclear reaction.
- Stable neutron:proton ratios change as atomic number increases (neutron:proton ratios increase from 1:1 to a higher proportion of neutrons, as nuclei get bigger)

Neutrino / Antineutrino emission

The anti-neutrino is the anti-particle of the neutrino. They are both identical except that a neutrino has *spin* $= \frac{1}{2}$ and an antineutrino has *spin* $= -\frac{1}{2}$ (spin is an angular momentum characteristic of a particle)

They both:
have zero charge
have zero mass ($\approx \frac{1}{2000} \times mass\ of\ electron$)
travel at speed of light
do not interact with matter (pass straight through, unaffected)
have spin $= \pm\frac{1}{2}$ ($+\frac{1}{2}$ *neutrino*, $-\frac{1}{2}$ *antineutrino*)

symbols: *neutrino* : v *antineutrino* : $\bar{v}$

Neutrino or antineutrino emission was shown to accompany beta-emission, since $\beta - particles$ are emitted with a range of energies. This is not be possible unless the decay also emits a third particle (in addition to the daughter nucleus and a beta-particle).

The diagrams on the next page helps to explain this:

Without third particle:

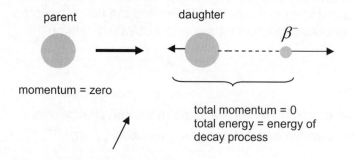

parent   daughter

momentum = zero

total momentum = 0
total energy = energy of
decay process

NOT POSSIBLE – BECAUSE:

This kind of two-particle interaction, where momentum is conserved and energy of products is equal to a certain energy, according to the decay process, would mean that the beta particle would have to have a certain energy.

However, it is observed that beta-particles are emitted with a continuous range of values. This can only be possible if a third particle is also emitted, as follows:

With third particle:

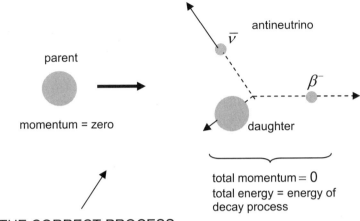

antineutrino
$\overline{v}$

parent

β^-

momentum = zero

daughter

total momentum = 0
total energy = energy of decay process

THE CORRECT PROCESS

Since there are an infinite number of ways to draw the three momentum vectors so that resultant momentum = zero (just like there are an infinite numbers of ways of drawing a triangle) it is now possible for the beta-particle emitted to have a range of energies – the neutrino (or antineutrino as shown here) can also have any energy (and momentum).

The full beta-particle decay processes are thus:

β^- decay $parent \rightarrow daughter + electron\ (\beta^-) + antineutrino\ (^0_0\overline{v})$

β^+ decay $parent \rightarrow daughter + positron\ (\beta^+) + neutrino\ (^0_0 v)$

(try writing equations using previous 2 examples, but include neutrinos/antineutrinos)

Decay Law (for Radioactive decay)

There are two versions of the decay law. The first states that the activity of a radioactive sample is proportional to the number of radioactive nuclei present. This is equivalent to saying that the rate of disintegration of a radioactive sample is proportional to the number of radioactive nuclei present. ie.

$\dfrac{dN}{dt} \propto N$, where, $N = number\ of\ radioactive\ nuclei\ at\ time, t$

$\Rightarrow \dfrac{dN}{dt} = -\lambda N$,where, $\lambda = radioactive\ decay\ constant, \dfrac{dN}{dt} = rate\ of\ decay$

The second form can be derived from the first by integration (not required for this course) and is as follows:

$N_0 = number\ of\ radioactive\ nuclei\ present\ initially$

$N = N_0 e^{-\lambda t}$, where, $N = number\ present\ at\ time, t$

$\lambda = decay\ constant$

Example T13.12

A tree dies, and, on its death, contains 2.2×10^{19} atoms of carbon-14, which is radioactive and has a half life of 5730 years. The tree is then buried underground and remains for many years. Given that the decay constant for C–14 is $1.21 \times 10^{-4} \, years^{-1}$, calculate the number of radioactive atoms per gram remaining after (a) 2000 years (b) 5730 years

Note that the answer to part (b) does not need to involve the use of the decay law equation, since 5730 years is equal to a whole half-life – and the amount remaining after one half life is half what you had to start with.

Derivation of Equation: $\lambda = \dfrac{\ln 2}{T_{1/2}}$, **where** $T_{1/2} = $ **half life**

Referring to: $N = N_0 e^{-\lambda t}$

After one half life has passed half the amount initially present has decayed, so,
$N = N_0/2$ when $t = T_{1/2}$. Hence,

$$N_0/2 = N_0 e^{-\left(\lambda T_{1/2}\right)}$$

$$\Rightarrow \tfrac{1}{2} = e^{-\left(\lambda T_{1/2}\right)} \Rightarrow 2^{-1} = e^{-\left(\lambda T_{1/2}\right)} \Rightarrow \ln 2^{-1} = \ln e^{-\left(\lambda T_{1/2}\right)}$$

$$\Rightarrow -\ln 2 = -\lambda T_{1/2} \ln e \Rightarrow -\ln 2 = -\lambda T_{1/2}$$

$$\Rightarrow \lambda = \dfrac{\ln 2}{T_{1/2}}$$

Example T13.13

A sample of a radioactive isotope contains 10^{18} atoms initially and has a half life of 10 hours.
(a) sketch a graph showing how the number of radioactive nuclei change for the first 30 hours
(b) Find the amount remaining after 10 hours
(c) calculate the decay constant and hence find the amount remaining after 1 day

Note that λ must be compatible with units of $T_{1/2}$ (e.g. NOT *seconds*$^{-1}$ *with hours* - convert $T_{1/2}$ to "same" units as λ)

Topic Fourteen: Digital Technology

Analogue and Digital Signals

An analogue signal is a signal that is continuously and infinitely variable: it can take an infinite number of possible "values"

A digital signal is a signal that can only take certain values

A voltmeter, for example, with a pointer needle is considered to be analogue – since the pointer has an infinite number of places/positions where it can point

Whereas a voltmeter with a digital (numerical) readout is considered digital because the readout can only have a finite number of values (a 3 digit voltmeter, for example, has 1000 possible values, including 0V)

Signals are often transmitted electronically and analogue signals can be converted into digital ones. This conversion is never 100% accurate, but digital signals are easier to transmit and reproduce without loss of quality or information of the signal.

Digital signals use the binary system to carry information.

The binary system is a system of numbers using only 2 characters: 1 and 0

We can use these numbers to represent colours (hence pictures), letters (hence text), or sounds or any other form of information.

Converting base 10 (the "everyday" number system) to base 2 (binary):

1 = 1
2 = 10
3 = 11
4 = 100
5 = 101

Etc.

It is easy to see how the system is increased but a little more difficult to understand.

The table below explains

Base 10 (denary) 378 in base 10				Base 2 (binary) 1011 in base 2			
1000s	100s	10s	units	8s	4s	2s	1s
10^3	10^2	10^1	10^0	2^3	2^2	2^1	2^0
Example:	3	7	8	1	0	1	1
	3×10^2	7×10^1	8×10^0	1×2^3	0×2^2	1×2^1	1×2^0
= 300 + 70 + 8 = 378				= 8 + 0 + 2 + 1 = 11 (conversion to base 10)			

Example T14.1

   (a) Write 50 (base 10) as a binary number.
   (b) Write 11011 (binary) as a base 10 number

Bits and Bytes

The word bit is short for binary digit.

For computer storage, there are 8 bits to one byte.

So, the binary number 101100 is a 6 bit number. The storage required for this would by 0.75 bytes.

Computers use ASCII code to represent letters and other codes.

Each ASCII code is exactly 1 byte, since ASCII codes are always 8 bit.

Example: 0100 0001 = ASCII code for A
               0100 0010 = ASCII code for B etc.

LSBs and MSBs

LSB = Least significant bit
MSB = Most Significant bit

The least significant bit is the right-most digit on a binary number
The most significant bit if the left-most digit on a binary number

Example T14.2

Convert the base 10 number 25 into a 5 bit binary number and state the value (size) of the LSB and the MSB

Examples of Storage of Information

(For illustrations do an internet search on digital analogue and the name of the device (e.g vinyl record)

Vinyl Record: The shape of the groove is used to create sound. This shape represents analogue storage of information since it can be any shape.

Audo Tape: The magnetic tape stores continuously varying information (a varying magnetic field) that can be used to create sound. It is another example of analogue storage.

Modern music systems; CDs DVDs, MP3 players etc. are all digital information storage devices. Light is reflected on to a disk and it is either reflected (1) or not (0). Repeated reflections give us the coding for information.

Reading information from a CD

A laser light is used. It is shone on to the CD where there are a series of pits. The interferences between reflected light and incident light can be read as intensity variations and as binary codes.

The following diagram will help me to explain further:

From Computer Desktop Encyclopedia
© 1998 The Computer Language Co. Inc.

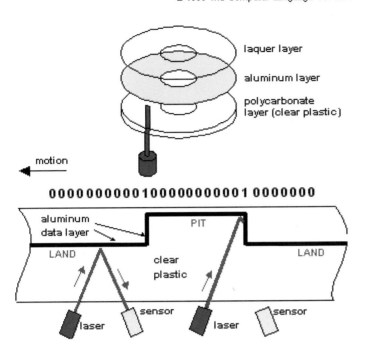

00000000001000000000001 0000000

As the CD rotates, light from the laser is directed towards the "pits" and "land". When there is a change from pit → land or land → pit the reflected light ray will be out of phase with the incident ray. Destructive interference will occur and there will be a "blink". Each blink is read as a 1. No change results in a 0.

The pit height necessary for a CD to work properly will depend on the wavelength of light used.

To work correctly destructive interference must occur between incident light and light reflected. For this to be true, the pit height must be a quarter of the wavelength of light used.

Example T14.3

A CD player uses laser light of wavelength 780nm. On refraction, as it enters the CD medium, its wavelength reduces to 500nm. For effective reading, what pit depth should the CD have?

Storage capacity

There are several ways to increase the storage capacity of a disk, as follows:

- Use higher frequency, smaller wavelength laser light. This means the pit size can be smaller and more pits can be used on one disk

- Increase the number of tracks by making the tracks (of land/pits) closer together

- Use dual or multiple layers. Double layer disks, for example, have a semi reflective upper layer coating so that some light can pass through to read the lower layer.

DVDs use all of the above features to give them a much higher storage capacity than Cds.

Comparison Digital versus Analogue

Real life signals (such as what you see and what you hear) are analogue signals: the colours change smoothly without digitalised pixels and the sound has an infinite variety of loudness and pitch.

Digital signals, therefore cannot possibly be exact copies of the real thing.

Some people would argue that the quality of an analogue photograph, using light falling on photosensitive paper, is superior to a digital photo.

Some argue that the sound produced from a digital CD is not as good as that produced from an old vinyl record, for similar reasons (the sound is not so natural).

The quality of an analogue signal, therefore, can be considered better than that of a digital signal.

However, digital information storage has the following advantages over analogue storage:

- Exact replication is very easy
- Reproduction and recording is easy and without the introduction of noise signals (unwanted signals). Analogue recording usually introduces noise.
- Signals can be easily transported over very large distances and cleaned (removing any noise picked up during transit through a cable) so that the received signal is identical to the one broadcast.
- Retrieval speed is much greater, since laser light and other electronic devices can be used for reading.
- Data can easily be manipulated (e.g computer enhancement of pictures, and computer sound editing)

A disadvantage of digital storage of information is that data loss can be catastrophic (e.g. hard drive failure) and over-reliance can be dangerous.

Data Capture; Digital Imaging using charge-coupled devices

Capacitance

A capacitor is a device that stores electrical charge. If a potential difference (voltage) is applied to a pair of parallel plates (conductors) the plates become electrically charged. This system of parallel plates is called a capacitor. The capacitance of a capacitor is defined as follows:

Definition: The capacitance is the charge per unit potential difference that can be stored on a conductor/capacitor.

Equation: $C = \frac{Q}{V}$

The unit of capacitance is the farad (F).

From the above definition it is clear that $1F = 1CV^{-1}$

Example T14.4

Calculate the charge stored by a 4.0μF capacitor when a potential difference of 12V is applied.

Charged Coupled Devices (CCDs)

CCDs are used extensively in imaging devices such as digital cameras, camcorders, electron microscopes and astronomical telescopes.

The main principle by which they work is that the light striking the CCD surface causes ejection of electrons (the photoelectric effect).

This ejection of electrons constitutes charge. The amount of charge produced will depend on the brightness of light incident on the CCD.

A CCD consists of many smaller cells called pixels. Each pixel produces photoelectrons and charge and so an entire picture can be built up.

Electrodes attached to the pixels can pick up the charge as voltages. This information, along with the pixel position, is then digitised and stored.

Note that the photoelectric effect is the effect whereby the energy of a light photon is transferred to an electron when the light photon strikes a surface. The electron (from the surface) is thus ejected and is called a photoelectron.

Quantum Efficiency

It should be noted that not all light striking a pixel will be efficient in producing photoelectrons, as described above. The light may be reflected or simply pass through the pixel.

Quantum efficiency measures how well light can produce photoelectrons.

Definition: **The Quantum Efficiency of a pixel is the ratio of the number of emitted electrons to the number of incident light photons.**

Magnification

Magnification is simply a measure of the scale of the image on the CCD compared to the real object.

Definition: **The magnification of a CCD is defined to be the ratio of the length (or width, etc.) of the image on the CCD to the length (or width, etc.) of the object.**

Resolution

It light from two different but very close together objects fall on the same pixel of a CCD they will appear as a single object and this will not be resolved. In order to be just resolved the images of two distinct points must be at least two pixels apart.

To produce very high quality images we can apply the following principles:

- Low magnification (so that several pixels are used for a small part of the object
- High quantum efficiency (so that exposure time can be low and blurring minimised)
- High resolution (and this means that there will be a large number of pixels per unit area on the CCD – so small pixels)

CCDs are particularly useful when low exposure times are important (X ray imaging for example) or only very low light conditions are available, like in astronomy.

.......and that is rather an abrupt finish – but it is a finish!!

Good luck – go over these questions, keep testing yourself and try past IB questions.

Knock 'em out!!

Solutions to HL Sections

Topic 9

T9.1 Range = 8.1m Speed = 13ms^{-1} (12.7ms^{-1}). Assumptions: air resistance is negligible, ground is horizontal

T9.2 Optimum angle is 45° to the horizontal

T9.3 (a) (i) Height above ground = 28m (ii) It hits the green building 2m from the left edge (iii) It hits the green building at a speed of 16 ms^{-1} (b) the ball is projected at 7.84 ms^{-1}

T9.4 (i) (a) 6.27 x 10^7 Jkg^{-1} (b) 6.22 x 10^7 Jkg^{-1} (c) 3.52 x 10^7 Jkg^{-1}
(ii) (a) 3.14 x 10^9 J (b) 3.11 x 10^9 J (c) 1.76 x 10^9 J
(iii) (a) 2.44 x 10^7 J (b) 1.38 x 10^9 J
(iv) (a) 2.45 x 10^7 J (b) 2.45 x 10^9 J

The first answer is very close using either method. However the second answer is far higher using the latter method. This second method only works when the gravitational field strength is approximately constant. This is true over short distances (heights) like 50km, but when increasing height by 5000km the field strength is significantly lower.

T9.5 (i) (a) $-1.4 \times 10^{-6} NC^{-1}$ (b) $+1.4 \times 10^{-6} NC^{-1}$ (c) $+2.1 \times 10^{-6} NC^{-1}$
(ii) (a) $-2.3 \times 10^{-25} J$ (b) $+2.3 \times 10^{-25} J$ (c) $+4.6 \times 10^{-16} J$
(iii) $3.1 \times 10^{-25} J$ (change = final – initial)

T9.6 (a) $8.00 \times 10^{-7} J$ (b) $1.96 \times 10^4 ms^{-1}$ (equate kinetic energy to potential energy difference)

T9.7 67.5 V

T9.8 $9.8\ Nkg^{-1} m^{-1}$

T9.9 $1.3\ Vm^{-1}$

T9.10 Field lines should go inwards towards planets. Equipotentials should be perpendicular to field lines, forming "deformed egg" / "dumbbell" shapes.

T9.11 $-2.11 \times 10^6 Jkg^{-1}$

T9.12 (i) $-5.76 \times 10^{-6} V$ (ii) zero

T9.13 (i) Field lines radially outwards, equipotentials circles of increasing radii (non uniform field)

(ii) Field lines horizontal, parallel, equidistance going from positive plate to negative plate; equipotentials vertical, parallel, equidistant (uniform field)

T9.14 (i) $2400 ms^{-1}$ (ii) $11200 ms^{-1}$
T9.15 Its time period will be 2.8 $\sqrt{8}$ times greater

T9.16 $2.86 \times 10^{12} m$ about 19 times further from the sun (exact ratio = $\sqrt[3]{84^2}$)

T9.17 (take T = 1 day, convert to seconds, find r) Answer: $4.2 \times 10^7 m$ from centre of Earth. This equates to $3.6 \times 10^7 m$ from surface of Earth.

T9.18 $E_K = 3.1 \times 10^9 J$ $E_p = -6.2 \times 10^9 J$ $E_T = -3.1 \times 10^9 J$

Topic 10

T10.1 71g

T10.2 Stage 1: $2.5 \times 10^5 J$ work done ON gas Stage 2: $3.0 \times 10^5 J$ work done BY gas $(-3.0 \times 10^5 J$ work done ON gas). Net work done BY gas = $5 \times 10^4 J$

T10.3

	change in volume (m³)	thermal energy transfer	work done	change in internal energy
i)	0.001 increase	1000J added	100J by gas	900J increase
ii)	0.002 decrease	1000J added	200J on gas	1200J increase
iii)	.001 decrease	1000J added	zero	1100J increase
iv)	0.005 Increase	0J (insulated)	500J by gas	500J decrease
v)	0 (const vol)	800J added	zero	800J increase
vi)	0 (const vol)	600J removed	zero	600J decrease
vii)	0.02 decrease	1000J removed	2000J on gas	1000J increase

T10.4

Diagram A (Refer to diagram following)
1. This is an isochoric change and is brought about by adding thermal energy to the system. Both Q and ΔU are positive, $W = 0$
2. This is an isothermal expansion (the p-V line follows an isothermal). Work is done by the gas – the amount of work done corresponds to the area under that part of the curve – ie the total shaded red area and blue area. T is constant $\therefore \Delta U = 0, Q = W$ So the thermal energy must have been added to system.
3. This is another isochoric change, but this time thermal energy is transferred from the system. Both Q and ΔU are negative, $W = 0$
4. This is an isobaric change (contraction). $W = p\Delta V$ and is negative – work is done on (not by) the gas and the amount corresponds to the shaded blue area (under this part of the curve). It is brought about by transferring thermal energy from the system and reducing its temperature. $W < 0, Q < 0, \Delta U < 0$ (since temperature decreases) The overall effect of the cycle is that work is done by the gas – the net amount of work done is equal to the red shaded area (red+blue – blue).

Diagram B: (see diagram following)
1. This is an isobaric expansion. $W = p\Delta V$ and is positive – work is done by the gas and the amount corresponds to the shaded blue area (under this part of the curve). It is brought about by transferring thermal energy to the system and increasing its temperature. V increases $\therefore T$ increases $\therefore \Delta U > 0, W > 0, Q > 0$

2. This is an adiabatic compression. The work done on the gas is represented by the area under this part of the curve – i.e. the red area + the blue area. $Q = 0, W < 0, \Delta U > 0$ (temperature increases)

3. This is an isochoric (constant volume) change and energy is transferred from the system. Both ΔQ and ΔU are negative, $W = 0$ ($\frac{P}{T} = const$, P lower $\Rightarrow$ T lower $\Rightarrow$ ΔU negative)

The overall effect of the cycle is that work is done on the gas – the net amount of work done is equal to the red shaded area (red+blue – blue).

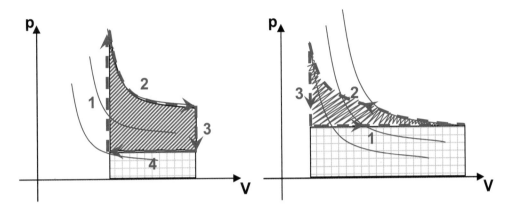

T10.5

Process	Q	W	ΔU
Isobaric contraction	< 0	< 0	< 0
Isothermal compression	< 0	< 0	0
Adiabatic expansion	0	> 0	< 0
Isochoric pressure drop	< 0	0	< 0
Isothermal expansion	> 0	> 0	0

T10.6

If heat from air moved into a much more concentrated space, like into a cup of water, the water would become hotter. Whilst this event **does not** violate the principle of conservation of energy, it **does** violate the law of entropy (the second law of thermodynamics) – the disorder associated with molecular motion has decreased.

Topic 11

T11.1

$$l = \frac{3\lambda}{2}(=1.5\lambda) \;\Rightarrow\; \lambda = \frac{2l}{3}$$

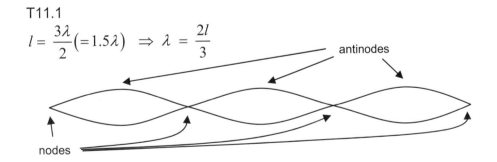

T11.2

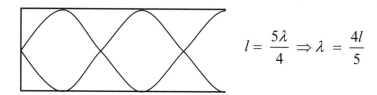

$$l = \frac{5\lambda}{4} \Rightarrow \lambda = \frac{4l}{5}$$

T11.3

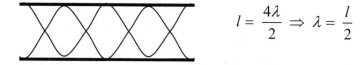

$$l = \frac{4\lambda}{2} \Rightarrow \lambda = \frac{l}{2}$$

T11.4

As the car travels past Asaf, the frequency he hears will decrease to 470Hz. As the car is approaching Buha she will hear the frequency as 559Hz.

T11.5 $1.6 \times 10^7 ms^{-1}$ away from the Earth

T11.6   (a) $0.0125\ radians$ (0.7°) (b) 11cm

T11.7   7.5m

T11.8 $I = 0.75I_0$ (25% reduction)

T11.9   34°

Topic 12

T12.1 $5.1 \times 10^{-4} Wb$

T12.2 $61 mWb$

T12.3   Aircraft is moving faster so rate of flux cutting is greater; angle at which flux is cut may be closer to 90°

T12.4   (a) $10.6 mV$ (b) $52.9 mV$

T12.5

(a) (i) as the coil begins to enter the magnetic field electrons on the right hand side will experience a force and there will be an induced current, upwards in the wire (using FRHR). Electrons actually experience a downwards force, and move downwards, opposite to conventional current direction. There will be an anti-clockwise current in the coil.

(ii) when the coil is moving through the field, electrons on the right hand side of the coil experience a downwards force, but electrons on the left of the coil also experience a downwards force these forces oppose each other so there is no overall current in the coil while it is completely in the field. It is important to note though, that there is an emf across the coil – there will be an excess of electrons on the bottom of the coil (as viewed from the page) and a deficit on the top.

(iii) as the coil begins to leave the magnetic field electrons on the right hand side are no longer affected by the field. Electrons on the left hand side continue to experience a downwards force, and therefore move downwards. Hence there will be a clockwise (conventional) current in the coil (opposite to direction of electron flow).

Note that there is no induced emf across the top or bottom part of the coil – electrons only experience a downwards force, not a horizontal force, in accordance with FLHR.

(b) Maximum current is attained when the coil is entering or leaving the field.
$\varepsilon = nBLv = 35 \times 35 \times 10^{-3} T \times 8.5 \times 10^{-2} m \times 0.1 ms^{-1} = 1.04 \times 10^{-2} V$

Using $V = IR, I = V/R \Rightarrow I = {}^{1.04 \times 10^{-2} V}/_{0.01\Omega} = 1.04 A$

Answer : $1.0A$

(c)

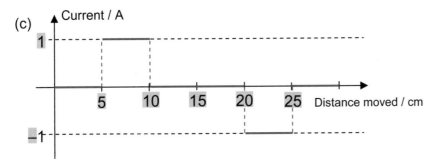

T12.6

There are two alternative ways of looking at this. One is to use FRHR, and consider the side of the loop nearest the wire as it moves towards the wire at this part of the loop. Using FRHR, there will be a current induced in the wire of the top part of the coil, going from right to left. So **there is an anti-clockwise current induced in the loop**.

The other method is to use Lenz's Law. There will be a current induced in the loop so as to oppose the change causing it. The change is the movement of the straight wire, so the current will be induced so as to repel the straight wire. The top part of the loop will therefore have current induced in it in the opposite direction of the straight wire so that the two wires repel. **There is therefore an anti-clockwise current induced in the loop.**

T12.7 8.5V

T12.8 340V

T12.9 (a) 8.3A   (b) 12A   (c) 29Ω

        (d) The heater will run on a lower power and put out less heat (per second) because a peak voltage of 240V is equivalent to ${}^{240}/_{\sqrt{2}} V = 170V$ d.c. Note also that halving voltage causes current to also halve (for the same resistance) and so power quarters. In this case power would reduce by a factor of $({}^{170}/_{240})^2 \approx 0.5$. So using a.c with peak voltage of 240V would result in only about half the power compared to running it with rms voltage of 240V.

T12.10 2500 turns

T12.11 (a) 192kW   (b) 19.2MW

Topic 13

13.1   (a) $2.23 eV$ (b) $2.88 \times 10^5 ms^{-1}$

13.2   (a) 0.236V   (b) 1.09V

T13.3 2.91nm

T13.4 $8.25 \times 10^6 ms^{-1}$

T13.5 (a) $2.18 \times 10^{-18} J$ (b) $3.28 \times 10^{15} Hz$

T13.6 (a) $0.70 eV$ (b) $n = 4\ to\ n = 3$

T13.7

Using the energy level diagram, I shall identify the wavelengths of light emitted when the electron jumps from $n = 3\ to\ n = 2$ and from $n = 4\ to\ n = 2$. Hopefully this will correspond to two of the lines in the spectrum shown (note that the spectrum only shows transitions to the $n = 2$ level, as stated).

$$E_{(4 \to 2)} = 3.4 - 0.8 = 2.6 eV$$
$$2.6 eV \approx 4.16 \times 10^{-19} J$$
$$E = \frac{hc}{\lambda} \Rightarrow \lambda = \frac{hc}{E} = \frac{hc}{4.16 \times 10^{-19}} m = 4.78 \times 10^{-7} m = 478 nm$$

This transition, from $n = 4\ to\ n = 2$, corresponds to the pale blue line shown towards the centre of the spectrum.

$$E_{(3 \to 2)} = 3.4 - 1.5 = 1.9 eV$$
$$1.9 eV = 3.04 \times 10^{-19} J$$

$$E = \frac{hc}{\lambda} \Rightarrow \lambda = \frac{hc}{E} = \frac{hc}{3.04 \times 10^{-19}} m = 6.54 \times 10^{-7} m = 654 nm$$

This transition, from $n = 3\ to\ n = 2$, corresponds to the red line shown on the diagram towards the right of the spectrum

T13.8

This happens because the radius of the path taken by positive ions is proportional to the mass:charge ratio. All hydrogen ions have a single positive charge, so the different paths cannot be explained by the fact that the ions may have different charges. The different path radii must therefore be explained by the fact that hydrogen has two isotopes – atoms with the same proton number but different mass numbers. Deuterium, for example, is the hydrogen isotope with mass number,2. This would result in a path in a mass spectrometer of twice the radius of the regular hydrogen ion, with mass number; 1.

T13.9

$\dfrac{m}{q} \propto r$, let $\dfrac{m_{(x)}}{q_{(x)}} = \dfrac{m}{q}$, then, as Y has twice the

charge and triple the mass, $\dfrac{m_{(y)}}{q_{(y)}} = \dfrac{3m}{2q} = 1.5\dfrac{m}{q}$.

Since the mass:charge ratio has increased by a factor of 1.5, so will the radius of the path. Hence the radius of the path taken by Y^{2+} is $1.5R$

T13.10

Carbon-14 has 14 nucleons, of which 6 are protons and 8 are neutrons. It is an unstable nucleus because it has a high neutron:proton ratio. It therefore decays by conversion of one of its neutrons into a proton and an electron. The neutron:proton ratio therefore changes from 8:6 = 4:3 (in C–14) to 7:7 = 1:1 (in N–14).

Reaction:

$^{14}_{6}C \rightarrow \ ^{14}_{7}N \ + \ ^{0}_{-1}\beta$. The radiation emitted is a negative beta-particle (electron)

$(+ \ \bar{\nu})$

T13.11

$^{22}_{11}Na \rightarrow \ ^{22}_{10}Ne \ + \ ^{0}_{1}e \ (+\nu)$

The sodium nucleus decays because its proton:neutron is too high for stability. It therefore decays by positron emission, whereby a proton changes into a neutron + a positron. The proton:neutron ratio changes from 11:11 (1:1) to 10:12 (5:6)

T13.12

(a) $N = N_0 e^{-\lambda t} = 2.2 \times 10^{19} e^{-(1.21 \times 10^{-4} \times 2000)} = 1.7 \times 10^{19}$

(b) $N = N_0 e^{-\lambda t} = 2.2 \times 10^{19} e^{-(1.21 \times 10^{-4} \times 5730)} = 1.1 \times 10^{19}$

T13.13

(a) To sketch the graph, one only needs to plot approximate coordinates after every 10 hours – and N drops by one half for every 10 hours

Note though, that the graph can be accurately plotted using the decay law equation, after first calculating the decay constant.

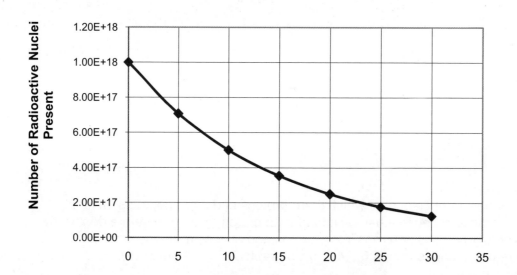

(b) 10 hours = 1 half life, so amount remaining after 10 hours = $\dfrac{(10^{18})}{2} = 5 \times 10^{17}$

(c) $\lambda = \dfrac{\ln 2}{T_{\frac{1}{2}}} = \dfrac{\ln 2}{10} = 0.069 \ hours^{-1}$

$N = N^0 e^{-\lambda t} = 10^{18} e^{-0.069 \times 24} = 1.9 \times 10^{17}$

Topic 14

T14.1 (a) 110010   (b) 27

T14.2 11001; LSB=1, MSB=16

T14.3 125nm

T14.5 $4.8 \times 10^{-5} V$